Drina Bridge

JIM BARTLEY

Drina Bridge

a novel

RAINCOAST BOOKS

Vancouver

Raincoast Books gratefully acknowledges the ongoing support of the Canada Council for the Arts, the British Columbia Arts Council and the Government of Canada through the Book Publishing Industry Development Program (BPIDP).

Jacket design by Teresa Bubela
Flap images (old paper) © Andrea Volpicelli/Dreamstime.com
Interior design by Tannice Goddard

Excerpt from *Wartime* by Milovan Djilas, English translation by Michael B. Petrovich, copyright © 1977 by Harcourt, Inc., reprinted by permission of the publisher.

LIBRARY AND ARCHIVES CANADA CATALOGUING IN PUBLICATION
Bartley, Jim
Drina Bridge/Jim Bartley.
ISBN 10 1-55192-959-7
ISBN 13 978-1-55192-959-0
1. Yugoslav War, 1991–1995 — Bosnia and Hercegovina — Fiction.
I. Title.
PS8553.A777D74 2006   C813 .54   C2005-905751-3

Library of Congress Control Number: 2006923676

Raincoast Books   *In the United States:*
9050 Shaughnessy Street   Publishers Group West
Vancouver, British Columbia   1700 Fourth Street
Canada v6p 6e5   Berkeley, California
www.raincoast.com   94710

Raincoast Books is committed to protecting the environment and to the responsible use of natural resources. We are working with suppliers and printers to phase out our use of paper produced from ancient forests. This book is printed with vegetable-based inks on 100% ancient-forest-free paper (100% post-consumer recycled), processed chlorine- and acid-free. For further information, visit our website at www.raincoast.com/publishing.

Printed in Canada by Friesens.

10 9 8 7 6 5 4 3 2 1

A Note on History and Fiction

The Yugoslavia that died in 1991 was built and sustained by Josip Broz Tito. The Partisan guerrilla leader and visionary socialist performed what many still consider a near-miracle. Out of the crucible of World War II, he forged a South Slav nation from rival Fascist, Royalist and Partisan camps and held its six constituent republics together for thirty-five years. A master at wielding both carrot and stick, he was loved for the prosperity and relative freedom he brought under Communism, and equally feared for his network of secret police and his ruthless purges of dissidents. Himself a mix of Croat and Slovene, he suppressed ethnic and national identities with an enforced policy of "Brotherhood and Unity." The veil he drew over old crimes and remembered pain was welcome. Thousands, perhaps millions of Serbs and Muslims, Croats and Slovenes, Montenegrins and Macedonians, re-invented themselves as Yugoslavs. When Tito died in 1980, people across the land wept openly in the streets.

His death began Yugoslavia's terminal illness. Over the next ten years, the power vacuum was filled by politicians fomenting and exploiting the revival of ethnic distinctions. When the communist states of Eastern Europe began to implode in the late 1980s, Yugoslavia's loose federation succumbed to a uniquely hellish collapse. The most ethnically integrated of the republics, Bosnia had been Tito's showpiece, a place where the dream of ethnic peace had become a way of life. In Sarajevo, one-third of marriages were mixed. Its schools and markets and neighbourhoods were filled with Muslims and Serbs and Croats who barely had a thought of their ethnicity. Until the nationalists and warlords made it a matter of life and death. By 1992 Bosnia was the new crucible of war.

Drina Bridge is a work of fiction, but it unfolds in a context that deserves meticulous attention to fact. Within the limiting framework of the story's settings, I have strived to present Yugoslav society and history honestly and accurately, in particular the wartime events of 1941-45 and 1991-95. The fiction is in the specifics of what happens to the central characters and also in a handful of the place names. There is in fact no monastery called Strastanica in Serbia, and no town, as far as I know, called Priječko. I've also invented other places in which fictional events occur: the Bosnian village of Mali Voćnjak, for instance, is fictional, but the larger events around Mali Voćnjak referred to in the book were actually happening in that region of Bosnia at that time. I've invented none of the major players in the political and military realm. Slobodan Milošević of course is real, or was, and I've taken pains to evoke him and other figures such as Radovan Karadžić and Ratko Mladić as authentically as possible — with the exception, of course, of certain satirical passages.

Readers who seek more Yugoslav facts and fictions might consider some of the books listed in my closing acknowledgements. But I hope you'll try this one first.

— JB

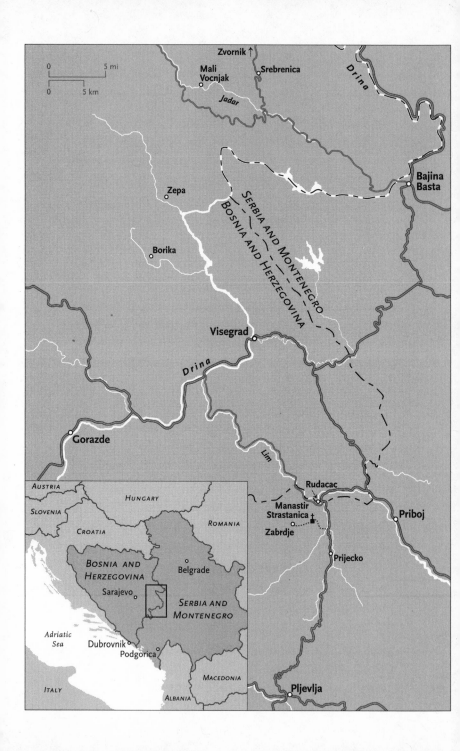

Again and again, even though we know love's landscape
and the little churchyard with its lamenting names
and the terrible reticent gorge in which the others
end: again and again the two of us go out together
under the ancient trees, lay ourselves down again and again
among the flowers, facing opposite the sky.

— RAINER MARIA RILKE
(TRANSLATION BY EDWARD SNOW)

Part One

Chapter One

BOSNIA, 1994

A basket of eyeballs. This I saw on the desk of General Zemko Izgorević, war hero of Serbia. There were other generals: Morcelle, the French one; McKenzie, the Canadian; an Israeli; a Dutch; and still others. The generals of peace. All hopeless venal masturbators awash in their own goodness.

But a basket, large and wicker, that once held twenty kilos of tomatoes — or onions, potatoes, bounteous things — now with a baker's large metal tray beneath to catch the drip of thin, cloudy fluid. Not blood, something else, the aqueous humour of eyeballs, clouded and slimed like runoff from a fishmonger's stall at day's end. I saw this with my own eyes, which were not in the basket, but still, temporarily, in my head.

I am writing without eyes. A problem? Do you doubt, gentle reader? But it is easy to write without eyes when you already have the advantage of writing without thumbs, as will become clear.

Why a basket of eyeballs? Because of this: the dupes who watch Slobo's (my evil twin) horror show beamed from Excrement

Central on all channels, who swallow this shit, who madly go into the countryside to slay the Fascist Ustashas and "Turks" who slew their parents or their parents' parents or their parents' parents' parents (I yawn now), these Serb mental zeros — yes, or Croat, Muslim, Mongol, Russian, Celt, Gaul, Yankee, lost angry boys everywhere — who are like magnetic tape, repeating any message that redistributes the particles in their boneheads, these are the boy-men who cannot bear to see the eyes of their victims before or after death. So, before or after death, the eyes are pulled out and the souls are destroyed. Or so they think. But not think, really, for it is all instinct and easy obedience, the dog army taught, then permitted, to nurture deepest hungers, tear out throats and swallow blood. The eyes are mumbo-jumbo insurance on a stolen patch of bleeding earth. They are also a proof of purchase to the General: Here, do you see? Three hundred dead Others. We regain our natural rights, lost by treachery to Them.

The General lifts the wicker lid, invites my gaze. I see shelled oysters. No. Mussels? Softboiled eggs, peeled and half-spoiled, sunk to a slithery mass?

"They are eyes," says General Izgorević, grease shining on his chin. Eyes of the dead. Well, some from the living too, no doubt. But no matter, they are all Ustashas. Blind anyway. Blind to the simple truth that baskets of innocent Serb eyes lead to larger ones full of Fascist Croat eyes. And some of these are also traitors' eyes. If they were fresher we would eat them for breakfast. Now we just serve them to lying Serb turncoats.

The general looks at me sharply. I leap across his desk and with remarkable speed and precision plunge my thumbs deeply into his eye sockets at the inner corners, hook my thumbs outward, pop out his orbs into my palms. Then I am shot in the back with the automatic weapons of two fake Rambos who have been standing at the door and who, by the way, smell like cattle in July. A dozen bullets pass through me and kill Izgorević instantly, depriving him of any proper appreciation of the justice I have wrought. But I am already dead, blood gushing from the exit crater over my heart.

Swearing, the Rambos gouge out my lifeless eyes with the intention of adding them to the basket, but are distracted by the raucous arrival of reinforcements from the bar downstairs. The mess is explained, then all turn to observe four faceless eyes on the General's blood-clotted carpet. Four eyes, deep brown, like strong Turkish coffee. The assembled Rambos stare. They grunt. They toss two eyes into the basket. Miming respect with their bulls' faces, they insert the other two into Izgorević's gaping sockets. Would that he could see through them. Yes, a few grams of me are mouldering in a Serbian hero's grave. The rest of me they threw down a poisoned well.

Everything you encounter here, voracious reader, is truth. Everything has happened. A dead man is speaking to you through the miracle of History. This is my death's work. The opus of an eternity. Amazing horrors. Blame and betrayal. I am Slobodan Kušić: Bosnian, village postmaster, occasional poet, witness of atrocity and folly. My parents were a Serb and a Muslim, an audacious coupling in 1930, their endorsement of a communal dream of peace. Tito's own dream. They named me Free (a talisman), just as our fearless leader's Montenegrin parents named him. And he has murdered thousands, no, tens, hundreds of thousands — not directly, but through calculated delegation and a master puppeteer's sleight of hand. He knows some history. He knows how to purblind foreign powers, giving them the profitable gift of ignorance. He catches fear on the wind and the scent of bile and wrath, and employs it. The result? Liberty! What a consummate joke.

And what an argument I had! In the railway station at Zabunac with Dušan, an old schoolmate and staunch Serb, who, with his greying fringe wild, his neck sinews like piano wire, shrieked at me of my duty. All the tired old deaths, the wars going back to the Flood almost. I told him I was leaving with the throng of farmers and villagers on the platform, all forced or dragged from their homes, shot, burned, nailed to trees, raped, these hundreds of survivors penned like livestock in the town arena, now evicted from there to be shunted somewhere else. It was said there would be a train soon, but some were leaving now, unchallenged by the armed drunks who knew they were no threat. They straggled west on the main road toward Sjecišta, a Muslim "Safe Zone" shattered daily by Serb ordnance. Gunfire came from the southeast; Dušan wanted me to join those guns against Islam: the jihad, a holy war that would engulf all Serbs and Croats and finally all of Europe. He began backing away, raving at me, said I was shitting on my father's grave, and my grandfather's too.

He was a cartoon of blood frenzy, a grizzled mad dog, old anger like poison in his veins, venomous foam on his twisting lips. He said I was throwing my poor dead mother into a Muslim cesspit, and his mother too, etcetera, etcetera. (Had he not known my mother was Muslim? Had he forgotten?) Then he stepped backward right off the platform and disappeared, flat out on the railbed. His head reappeared, then shoulders, then there was a *pop*, and another; the crowd on the platform heaved, and Dušan jerked and then slumped to the rails out of sight.

Someone in the crowd had shot him — the act of a madman.

The Rambo drunks waded in and threw people face down on the pavement, began a search. Then an ancient man, dried and gaunt like a mummy, tottering, began babbling at them, waving a little pistol. Two of the soldiers shot him at once with their machine guns — the Russian ones they all have, on all sides. Some others were hit with the spray of bullets. Those on the road began running, dropping bags, not looking back. People trying to leave the platform were shot in the back. I lost the thumb of my right hand from a shot that missed a boy of perhaps fourteen, while other bullets passed through him, spraying me with blood and flesh. I scrambled beneath a bench by the station wall and waited for the firing to end.

I am a record of subtraction. When I was a boy of eleven in Višegrad, cowering under a stone arch of the Drina Bridge, I lost my left thumb to a minor explosion in the war with Fascism. This particular bomb was Serbian. A slight alteration of circumstance would have made it German. Another shift might have seen it lobbed by Croat or Muslim Ustashas, by Serb or Croat or Muslim Partisans, or Montenegrin peasants allied to nothing but their own endangered village. Our fear before the enemy was as acute as our uncertainty of who the enemy ought to be. Fifty years later, on the day of his death by vengeance, Dušan said I must fight, at over sixty years of age, for the honour of my country. Would he like to see me fight now, with no thumbs at all?

It has been said that thumbs first made us superior to the animals. Not brains — God knows! With thumbs we made tools and toys. I remember a film in which ape-men beat each other with sticks, then astronauts were killed by a computer in outer space. History, gentle reader, is all thumbs.

Chapter Two

From my room I can see Stefan in the vegetable garden, his face tilted down at the tomato vines. His black robe is pressed to his body by a hot summer wind. Sun is full on him, columns of cloud piling up over the hills beyond. He reaches and cups a red orb in his hand, tugs it free, bends to set it in the basket at his feet. As he straightens up he seems to stare directly at me, though he can't possibly see me, here in the shadows. He returns to his task: salad for twenty.

We've been up to the lookout. Today we didn't talk about garden chores, or sheep, or the latest fasting directive. Stefan mentioned that his mother has a birthday approaching in Bosnia, so we found ourselves considering things from which there's no seclusion — the dark smoke on the horizon for instance. Yesterday, succumbing to my many offers, Stefan at last asked to see Slobodan's manuscript. After twenty pages he'd had his fill. From our clifftop bench this morning he looked across to the Bosnian border town of Rudačac, where there had once been a thin white pencil of a minaret against a green hill. "I will not learn more from this text. It's full of anger. I know his reasons, but it's not for me. It's for people outside."

I ask myself now if he meant outside the war or outside the cloister. Of course it's both. Stefan intimately knows this war and his faith. I know loss, and I've seen war, but Stefan's loving God eludes me. Three years here and I remain his implied outsider. I'm the goad to Stefan's certainties. He's the anchor against my drift. I consider faith a conjuring trick, a sleight-of-mind spurred by knowing the worst. But this place and Slobodan's memoir still urge me toward it.

I've stayed in touch with Axel: letters, an occasional phone call. I hear the sputter of his espresso machine or the yap of Oscar, his little schnauzer, and television, NewsWorld. We avoid talk of the war now. Satellite news streams into Axel's Front Street offices. He's wired in to the latest shocks. In the beginning he would tell me where the shells landed, the ones I'd heard a few hours before, far off, crumping on the morning air. From Toronto I got the body count in a besieged town a few kilometres across the Bosnian border. Axel implied that the gunners could just as easily blow up Jelenje Mountain, and that would be the end of me. But soldiers do not bomb their own holy men.

Axel wanted me home. We share an exuberant, at times a joyful past: also a tragic one. Together we witnessed Pimm's slow decline, then his terrible final months, in the house I shared with him on Dundonald Street. At first a challenge that we rose to, his illness at last descended to the nightmarish and stupefying. His body became a horror; it seemed a wonder that it still sustained him.

His mind slipped away. We monitored, we caressed, we tidied up, we each squeezed a hand as he died in a morphine haze.

Axel is my link to who I was, to my memory of Pimm alive, and the settling warmth I imagined would last forever. There's a plan for him to come here soon. September. He'll finally see me on site, meet the brothers. Then a drive down to Dubrovnik, a few days with Antonia. A reunion of sorts, stirring old affections.

Chapter Three

A few months before his death Pimm found his adoption records in our basement. They were buried in a box of Hoekstra family books and papers that hadn't been touched since his mother's death in 1981.

Pimm knew he'd been adopted, but he never seemed impelled to complicate his life with ancestral digging. At eight months he had become Pieter Erich Hoekstra (Pimm ever since) and lived briefly in Milan where his father's company did reconstruction work for the Italians after the war. From 1949 he had been raised in Amsterdam, until the family moved to Canada when he was sixteen. At some point he'd asked if his background was Italian, and his parents told him that he'd been born in Yugoslavia at the end of the war and had arrived in Italy in care of the Red Cross with a boatload of refugees. His father's fate was unknown and his mother was said to have died of pneumonia. Pimm had always said that Yugoslavia meant nothing to him. In the end, that changed.

I found a half-eaten dish of cantaloupe balls on the laundry-room table. Pimm had taken them to the basement in another of his sudden shifts to search mode. He was in the storage room, barely able to stand from exhaustion, the Hoekstra family archives scattered around him. This was better than finding him in the backyard in his pyjamas, as I had a few days before, with a shovel beside him, and holding the muddy cigar-box coffin of Max, his beloved ferret. "I want him under the flowering cherry." The cherry was in the front yard. I looked at Pimm, looking down at the dirty, nicked wooden box like it was the repository for all things lost, and I picked up the shovel. While he sat on the porch steps still in his pyjamas, I reburied Max. Pimm went inside and plucked a white gardenia blossom from one of his birthday plants, and we laid it on the fresh earth.

Now he had dug up something else: a birth certificate that we hadn't known existed, from Yugoslavia, yellowed and smudged and rubber-stamped, and entirely in impenetrable Cyrillic. The birth date was the giveaway: 23 Maj 1945. Attached were his adoption papers. The Italian was easier to decipher. Birth name: Saša Kožić. Mother: Ljiljana Kožić (deceased). Father: unknown. Nothing had changed of course. But Pimm's face when he scanned these documents had a look between affrontedness and wonder. Who was this Saša Kožić? From what was he created? I could see him thinking it — that something essential was missing.

He's been dead five years — a third of our time together. We met when I was twenty-one and Pimm thirty. Here I've turned forty. I don't grieve now except very rarely in the wee hours, spurred sometimes by the sound of the brothers at matins. Sweet memories drift up. Our sacred and giddy Thursday nights with the choir at St. Thomas's. Pimm in from the office with a fresh bottle of gin and a new CD, ice clinking into the glass. He loved church music with the fervour of a man who had no truck with sin or penance.

On a November night in 1987, 6 p.m. and the sky already black, Pimm walked into our kitchen, shook out his sodden umbrella and said, as if mildly put off by the weather, "Well, it looks like I'm positive." Weeks before, he'd mentioned a test. We'd already had them done once, a precaution. I looked up from my peeled garlics and we stared at each other. There was a soft pleading in his eyes. I'm not sure what my eyes held. It felt like anger. It probably showed as anger, but I put down my knife and hugged him, and it felt like I was forgiving him. I attacked the garlic cloves and sliced into the flesh of my thumb. The flow of blood was shocking. Pimm bandaged me and made dinner. He kept asking, "Are you all right? Poor Chris." These scenes keep returning to me.

By 1990 Pimm existed on a few dozen pills and hardly more calories per day, and needed constant medical and personal support to remain barely functional. In this state he pursued his Mystery of Origins. He began demanding maps and travel guides, planning an itinerary for a summer jaunt through Serbia and Montenegro, to climax with an extended stay at the town in which he, Saša Kožić, was born in the spring of 1945. That town was, is, Priječko, about ten kilometres from Strastanica Monastery, three of them down a precipitous twisting track to a valley road that follows the river Kriva, snaking its way north to the Bosnian border.

There are other things here that raise the past. Events only a few hours' drive from Strastanica, in the madness of Bosnia, still return Pimm's last days to me, spurring something like grief, but more encompassing. Grief is singular, a personal black hole. Here I've looked into a black pit dug for others. This year the pit has only gaped larger. I'm living in a place where beauty and agony have no distance between them.

We have a monk here named Krzić. Pimm, while he could still focus on a page and a thought, would scan the Toronto phone book for names like that, ring hapless strangers, bewilder them with his story, hang up undaunted, phone someone else. I told him as gently as I could that the project could be delayed, that a long journey would only exhaust him. Of course we could take a holiday, but right now he needed rest. (How could I say the truth? *This trip would kill you.*) He refused to be swayed. He tried to phone Kožićs in Priječko, got into shouting matches with the operators. I would leave the bedroom, leave him to whatever homecare worker was assigned that day to care for a man who rejected food, medicine and clean sheets in favour of scratching notes on a dog-eared map or reading the same page of a travel book over and over.

Then he was gone. So my first trip to Yugoslavia was for him, a journey that looked back and forward at the same time, once the worst grief was wrung dry. I embarked on his last plan, his extravagant quest for who he was, and it grew into my own plan.

Chapter Four

In September of 1991 Serbia and Croatia were at war. The CBC handed Axel a two-week assignment to Dalmatia. His base would be Dubrovnik, the walled, medieval city on the Adriatic. He said I wasn't to worry, the city was far from the fighting and well protected, a national treasure. As he gave me the details on the phone I felt something surging through me. I told him I was going with him — quickly promising to stay out of his way. I suggested he might be glad to have a friend handy for the empty evenings, someone to help him decompress after hard days. To that he quickly agreed. I think we both knew what hadn't been said: I had to rouse myself, get back into the world.

When I got off the phone I found one of Pimm's maps and scanned the coastline of Croatia, following the highway running south into Montenegro, then inland. It was perhaps five hours by car from Dubrovnik to Pimm's pencilled circle around the Serbian town of Priječko. I got back on the phone and by evening I had myself booked with Axel and crew. Three days later we were in Zagreb airport awaiting a flight to the coast. As we sampled some Karlovac beer, I opened my map on the bar.

"Look. Pimm was born here, or near here. A little town in the mountains: Pri-yetch-ko."

Axel stared at the map, then narrowly at me: "We can't go there, don't even think about it. There's a war on. I'm on assignment. And I certainly won't let you go alone."

I kept my eyes on the map.

The marble streets of Dubrovnik were empty of tourists. Soldiers patrolled the fringes of the Old Town. There were gun emplacements on the city walls. While Axel pursued his story I made the rounds of the travel offices. My phrase-book Croatian brought replies in pointed English. I was told to banish any thought of entering Serbia. One woman was candid: I was to enjoy Dubrovnik while it was still here.

The city seemed carved from one giant piece of fawn-coloured marble. Vehicles were forbidden inside the walls. The sounds were voices, footsteps on stone, the coo and swoop of pigeons, trundling handcarts. Bells rang out the noon hour from competing towers. In a deserted restaurant I ate oysters and garlicky calamari, then I climbed a stepped street to the wall and stared at the glinting Adriatic. I wondered if Saša Kožić's escape to Italy had begun from Dubrovnik harbour. That thought led me to the office of the port authority, hoping they would have an archive. When my stumbling questions raised a glimmer, it seemed that they might — and they weren't going to let me near it.

Within days, Axel's news nose homed in on Antonia Perović, a Yugoslav-American historian. Based in New York, she was in

Dubrovnik for a conference that mostly wasn't happening; all but a handful of participants had cancelled. Toni became our knowing guide to Yugoslavia's dissolution. Before Axel's camera she evoked terrors and retribution with her histories of sieges and kings and marble saints. We learned she had been raised in Novi Sad, Serbia's second city. Her mother was Istrian Italian, her father's family Serbs for generations. She still had a time share in Kotor, just down the coast. Over dinner with Toni we heard her assessment of what was to come. "We're going back. Fifty years. And now there's no more Tito to take the moral high ground. We're all Fascists and Chetniks now, like it or not. Our leaders are feeding us poison and people are ready to swallow it." She hadn't been quite so candid for the cameras.

There were power outages, then only cold water in the Hotel Lastovo's taps. Breakfast one morning was canned fruit and tepid, undrinkable coffee. We found a place in town that was still serving grilled fish and convened there nights with Toni. At one of these dinners Axel described my abortive visit to the port authority, and it became my opening for letting Toni in on the Pimm saga. I hadn't mentioned him, had little desire to play the widow, but after Axel's anecdote I piped up.

"I was looking for passenger lists from the war. I had a friend, he died last year, but he was born in Yugoslavia. He got out after the war, on a refugee boat."

"Was he young?"

"Forty-five. I mean ..." Toni gazed steadily at me. "I mean he was a child of course, when he got out, an infant. A Dutch couple adopted him and they eventually moved to Canada. Before he died he had plans to come here and do some ancestral research."

"He was from Dubrovnik?"

"Priječko. In the Sandjak region. I thought I might rent a car but ..."

"Not a chance."

"Seems not. But someday."

"Someday. Yes. I'm sorry to hear about your friend. What was his name?"

"Saša Kožić."

"A Serb, I would guess."

"That doesn't matter to me."

"It will in Sandjak."

Axel pushed the fish bones around on his plate. He glanced at Toni. "He's got an itch."

Toni looked me over: "Well, best to cool it for a while."

Back at the hotel, on impulse, I looked in the Dubrovnik phone book for Kožićs. There were none. When I joined Axel in his room he was viewing the day's footage: Croatian talking heads. Most were measured voices, or at least guarded. A handful were calmly virulent. Serbs were animals, barbarians. When aroused, said a suited man in a book-lined office, they attained an "atavistic bestiality." Toni commented later, "His daughter might have married one."

One morning, Belgrade's warships appeared. From my balcony Axel and I squinted at the flotilla off a point of land to the south. The hotel advised that they were closing immediately and gave us the name of another, further inland. By noon we were pacing in the new room, the TV playing images of shells throwing up geysers of water in the harbour. The Yugoslav People's Navy spent the next few hours casually destroying every ferry and pleasure boat in Dubrovnik's marina. Then there came a calm as night set in. Before dawn the next morning we were on a packed bus to the airport. Axel had his story.

Chapter Five

It was Toni who suggested the monastery. I stayed in touch, calling
her often in New York for her take on the news. I began to sleep
on the fold-out bed in the sun room. Waking early, to daylight,
helped me to get started. I ate anywhere but at a table. After a false
retreat the memory beast was finding new routes to me, through
furniture, silent rooms, the objects on shelves and walls. Clear
images came up. Pimm papering the guest room, stirring a pot in
his striped apron, sunning on the deck with a straw hat over his
crotch. Each picture brought a rush of tenderness, then crushed
me. That winter I read stacks of books and articles on Yugoslavia.
I took a course in basic Serbo-Croatian. My tutor, a Yugoslav,
wouldn't comment on the war, but she made sure I knew by heart
the handful of idiomatic differences marking Serbs from Croats.

One morning I called the agent who'd sold us the house eight
years before. Then I called Axel at work.

"Where will you go?"

"I'll find an apartment. I need to pare things down."

"Stay with me. I'll help you with the house. Stay as long as you
need to."

"I'll probably be away most of the summer."

"Whatever. You're beyond welcome, you know that."

"I could walk Oscar."

"You're a brave man."

The war in Croatia ran its course. Toni called it a pointless waste from start to finish, the outcome never in doubt. It was a war of *inat*, she said, adding that "spite" was the closest English equivalent, but didn't come near the mythic power of the word. Resigned to Croatian independence, Slobodan Milošević turned his ambitions elsewhere. By March the conflict had shifted to Bosnia. Toni agreed there was little chance I'd find bullets flying in Sandjak. She warned me off motels.

"You're near Pljevlja, yes?"

"Priječko."

"Right. Pljevlja, Priječko, Priboj. It's a triangle."

"I guess it is."

"There's a monastery nearby. Strastanica. It's known for its frescos and icons. These places are always short of cash for restoration, even for basic maintenance. Tito left them to rot. I think I was at this place when I was girl. I've been talking to a colleague in Belgrade. Strastanica has a guest quarters, probably quite empty right now. Mira was there a few years ago on a study tour. It's worth looking into. Your money would be well spent. The area is gorgeous, by the way."

"Will they try to convert me?"

"They'll just take the cash. Phone Mira, she'll get you rolling. You might even come down to Nikšić for a visit. I'll be seeing my sister there in August, if you're still around."

Mira had worked with church officials assessing the frescos at Strastanica and elsewhere. She suggested I fax her a note addressed to Abbot Nikolaj, telling him my plans and the reports I'd heard of the monastery's hospitality, and offering an unspecified donation. She would translate and mail it to Strastanica. About a month later the Abbot's reply came. I was welcome.

The house sold quickly. I kept photos, a few books and mementoes. Axel got the art. The rest was cleared out for sale or storage. I didn't even begin an apartment search. By the end of May I was on a plane to Belgrade. A long bus ride would take me to Serbia's mountainous western border with Montenegro and Bosnia, where I was booked into Manastir Strastanica for three months. Axel was a little surprised. Three months? In a monastery? But I saw the time flitting by, with nothing to come home to.

Chapter Six

We lived in a house hard by a bubbling stream, my uncle Vaso's. So lucky we were! The war raged and we heard it only on the wind. A hillside in the mountains of Kupojno, with rushing water to soften the buzz of war planes. A solitary house in a cradle of craggy rock, with birch and tall black pine trees for a natural blind, a shingled roof obscured with moss. With a few sheep and goats, some chickens, one old dog, a fat pig awaiting her slit throat. Hardly a target even if spotted.

A house with a bony scarecrow of an uncle who ate like a starved dog and coughed and rattled like death. He hit me in the face when I was bad. Then he would be as indifferent as if I were a broom in the corner. Afterwards he would tickle my nose with his moustache that stank of tobacco. He would make pebbles disappear and find them in my pocket. My Aunt Marija was younger, plumper, ever in motion until she dropped each night into bed. She complained of her burden, collapsed and wept, then picked it up and resumed. She kept me and my sister and her two boys busy and fed. She shouted at me to be careful before I went out to the stream, to lower my homemade net into the chill water and scoop up the little fish that Uncle smoked on a woodfire behind the house, but on cloudy days only, when there were no planes.

The planes came over, disappeared beyond the hills. Sometimes from far away we could hear the faint sound of explosions. The planes came back, ignoring or not seeing us. My uncle exclaimed yet again, his flat joke, "Flying Frankfurters!" He would sometimes add, heavy with contempt, "A race of dogs."

A truck came. Uncle saw it at a distance on the road below. Trucks or tanks would go past on the valley road, on their way to the chaos that had spared our area. Would they turn up our track? This was always the question. This truck turned as if planned. Uncle met the men a short distance from the house. An Ustasha officer got out of the truck with a pistol. The driver stayed in the cab with a rifle aimed at Uncle. Five or six soldiers jumped casually from the rear and trained their weapons on the house. Uncle was searched, then they marched him up to the house and came inside. They wanted birth and marriage records. Uncle then told them with nervous dignity what he could not hide, what they knew already from our fear, and from the small divergences of speech and household gods that render we South Slavs alien to one another even as we share our boiled Turkish coffee and raise toasts with glasses of identical plum brandy. He told them we were Serbs. (Not precisely true for Vedrana and me: our absent Partisan father, Uncle's brother, was Serb, our mother Muslim).

We sat in the kitchen with two officers as the rest searched the house, knocking over furniture, breaking glass and china, shooting at the chickens from the windows. They found a wad of paper money in a jar in the cistern. They found Uncle's pistol in the meat locker, took him outside and shot him with it. I remember the spray of blood on the kitchen window. My sister began screaming and Aunt collapsed to the floor whimpering and praying. The men were drinking Uncle's brandy. Some of them took my sister into the bushes behind the house, where she eventually stopped screaming. She was fourteen. It was only Uncle that they killed. They took food, some chickens in a coop, they shot our pig and quickly bled and gutted it, threw it in the back of the truck, and they left.

As it happens, these events did not occur at my uncle's house, although Ustashas were in those mountains later that year, dragging Serbs from their houses and killing them in many imaginative ways. What happened was this: a truck full of Serb Royalists, of Chetniks, arrived. Chetniks did not kill fellow Serbs unless those Serbs were traitors allied with Tito's Partisans, or with Italians, or with ... but it was and is impossible to keep up with alliances and betrayals. These Chetniks did not kill us, although they smelled like horses and behaved very badly, and their pathetic truck was half-crumpled and pocked with bullet holes. They wanted food, and began loading their truck with it. They shot our pig and bled it.

Then we heard planes. The Chetniks became agitated. They moved their truck quickly under some trees, then changed their minds. They threw the pig into the truck and left in a hurry. The planes went over and then one of them turned, returning in a lazy circle. Uncle stared at the sky, then forced us from the house running, we had never moved so fast, running to the sheep meadow, all of us and the dog too, flat on the ground behind the largest of the old Bogomil stones. The plane dropped a bomb in the valley, perhaps impeding or killing the fleeing Chetniks. Then it went over the house once, circled back, dropped one bomb, which destroyed the henhouse and part of the kitchen. It came back again. The German bombardier, his own house destroyed later in Berlin or Dresden, hit our house very precisely this time. Uncle ran screaming across the meadow after the departing plane, stood bellowing curses. Then he dropped to his knees, coughing and cursing.

Aunt led us toward the house, told us to stay clear. She was dry-eyed, staring as if at a strange foreign landscape. Dust and feathers were settling, revealing in the yard, in the vegetable patch, broken furniture, roof tiles, our smashed beds, split timbers, sections of wall. A splintered chair was wedged in the branches of the beech tree. Two outer walls stood tall but broken, and as we watched, one slumped with a crumble of mortar, tottered, then crashed with a cloud of white dust into the cellar, burying Aunt's shelves of preserves. Our old Alsatian, Garo, bewildered but uninjured, sniffed at the hens' blood soaking into the earth. Uncle was still on his knees in the sheepmeadow as Aunt came to her senses, and began to wail.

JUNE 1942
MY INITIATION

I found myself in a garage where trucks had once been. There were engine parts and piles of large rotted tires, oil like thick sludge on the stone floor, splattered even on the stone and timber of the walls. This had been a cow or a horse barn once, but years of oil and grease had covered any trace of animal presence. Here

I languished for two weeks, sleeping on a straw pallet. I heard fighting sometimes at a distance, sounds of tanks and trucks, planes. I was locked in, seeing sky and treetops from small high windows. On a promise of help, the German lieutenant had brought me from Višegrad bridge. His actions were measured and cunning, and led me to endure more absurdities, indignities and mad panics.

This German might as easily have been Italian, or filled with any other sort of blood. And if not a lieutenant, then perhaps a potato farmer, a tax collector, the caretaker of a school, a criminal escaped from a jail or government agency. I did not experience the German lieutenant in his military capacity at all (unless this was the rubric under which he imprisoned me — but can a ten-year-old be a military prisoner?). Regardless, his essence in those few weeks was not especially German or soldierly. He was simply a man, with a man's hands and power, and, I am compelled to add, a man's reproductive equipment. Though I could hardly have been a party to reproduction, he insisted on miming a travesty of that sacred ritual: he regularly performed an intent to impale me, although he always stopped short of entry. Whether he denied himself insertion out of charity or fastidiousness, I do not know. His heat for me made him moan and tremble. He had golden hair and noble features, like the lithe young Nazis in a Riefenstahl movie. Had he been an uncle or cousin, and kept his hands off of me, I might have emulated his pure manliness. As it was, I grew progressively colder, harder, like a block of wood or stone, an inert doll in his groping hands.

He would come to me sometimes nightly, sometimes every second night, always alone, always with water and some food. After the fumbling sex act he would linger, a spectre of false regret. He would encourage me to eat. In the mean glare of an oil lamp, he would gnaw on smoked sausage and stale bread to demonstrate its goodness. His prominent jaw muscles flexed and twitched. He left matches and oil for the lamp, hung a wire to suspend it, warning me of fire danger. He would talk to me in his language, chewing, watching me, but he was talking to himself, weighing the dilemma that was me, his use of me. Then he would switch to stiff Serbo-Croatian. Nodding, chewing, he would urge me to eat, forcing a sick smile through his bolus of sausage. He harboured the strange illusion that he was a kindly man. I grew to hate his smell, the bruised onion scent of guilt. I never ate with him, and he would finally leave me, locked in with the rotten tires and engine grease.

War offers unique opportunities. I saw that I had an opportunity to kill my enemy. It had been possible since the beginning, but not at once obvious to a subdued child. Strewn about were parts of machinery: pistons, camshafts, gears and levers — an assortment of crude weapons. I planned his death, my heart leaping with each imagining. With clarity of mind borne on the hope of freedom, I noted the minutiae of our sad dance, when and how he became most vulnerable, where I might conceal the object that would crush his skull. The anticipation of failure panicked me. Would he smell my fear as he kissed and pawed at me? I delayed the deed. One night he arrived drunk, awash in dark sentiments, still pulling on a bottle. He sat staring myopically at things far off or buried inside himself, then began a monologue of despair or regret or God knows what. I didn't care what horror his war had visited on him or what might have been in his mind. He may even have determined it was time to kill me, and was now wallowing in his guilty power. Little Slobo pretended interest in his wallow, allowed an eventual groping carress. I had seen my own father as drunk and knew my lieutenant would soon pass out. When he did, I smashed the back of his head with my carefully concealed weapon, a machine lever with an arc of gear teeth at its end. How easily this piece of scrap iron broke through his skull — as if it were a melon! He sat up with a jerk and his eyes stared at me with wonder, then with nothing at all. He fell forward and his arms and legs began to twitch, aimless, like a half-crushed beetle. His blond hair was matted red and the hole in his skull showed grey-white brain inside, glistening in the lamplight. His throat made sucking sounds. I hit his head several more times until he stopped moving. I felt his life leave him, felt the instant when I was alone again, when my German lieutenant became meat and bone and offal. When my heart stopped racing I gathered the remaining food into my pockets and went out into the clear June night, where my own quivering brain dumbly recorded a silver crescent of moon and winking stars.

I began walking. After a few minutes I stopped. I returned and upset the oil lamp onto my straw bed and put a match to it, and then I ran.

Chance divides the actual from the true. The actual might avoid the true — for a time. But truth lurks eternal. It's always there, hovering closer to here.

Truly, Uncle Vaso's brain had not been unlike the German lieutenant's. My aunt knelt in the yard and cradled Uncle's head, smearing her apron. Blood ran from his nose and ears. One eye, blown out from behind, dangled on his cheek. He looked too fantastic to be real. Aunt stared at him like a halfwit, smoothing bloody hair over his forehead, then she turned her face to the sky and wailed, shrieked.

I was a little man and took the situation in hand, pulled her off and left her babbling, prostrate, among rubble and dead chickens. My sister crouched on the back steps with her head down, convulsively retching but dry. Three little men, two age nine, one ten, dragged Uncle's body to the softer ground near the exploded henhouse. We buried him and made a cross from broken planks tied with rope.

We cleared rubble and salvaged some furniture, our mattresses and blankets, pots, etcetera. We righted the woodstove where it had landed in the yard, and held together its broken panels with wire. Thereafter we cooked in the open. We began to live in a corner of the cellar with the splintered kitchen floor as our roof: my aunt, her two boys, myself, and my sister who stopped speaking, who barely ate, who screamed in the night. We had food: some dead chickens, eggs from surviving hens, potatoes, turnips, carrots, some smoked fish. The earth over Uncle's grave slowly sank, and a sweet stench hovered over it. The weeds grew thick. The summer advanced without incident, the war coming as always on the wind.

In late August the fighting came near. Two jeeps arrived: five Ustashas with an assortment of weapons. They stayed with us for several days. The commander sat on our best chair in the shade of the beech tree and watched the valley with binoculars. He sucked eggs. With a knife he expertly punched two holes in each egg. The shells were strewn beside his chair. Like all men in combat, he smelled. A part of me savoured his smell, the sweat of extremity, of men at the limit, stripped of trite pleasures, their lives honed to a taunting and courting of death. These soldiers might have killed us but they merely used us. They might have raped Aunt but for her age, or my sister but for her bony, unkempt, souring madness. They were unkind but not deadly, not even cruel. We had no men who needed killing. The commander offered that he did not allow rape, having daughters of his own. So, we were simply peripheral to their business.

When the soldiers pissed demonstratively in the yard I was duly impressed with the stream, with their flouting of decorum. I had a child's idea: that these powerful men would take me away with them. I was tired of a life of ruin and wailing. They had not killed my uncle. They had not harmed us. I might be their mascot. My sister and Aunt seemed like walking dead. Like all children I was indifferent to pain that was not my own. I was still capable of a naive wonder distinct from judgement or propriety. Escape meant leaving perhaps for a better ruin, one that would mean adventure, a ruin not viewed from inside defeat. I would sit in the jeep wedged between redolent warriors, admiring the strength of their large hands in repose. They would take me where I could freely leave them for my own warrior father, as if all soldiers were engaged in the same fierce and comradely enterprise. A stupid unformed child's idea, borne of ignorance and fantasy, hope, denial. That there was in fact *no* hope, that it was merest chance (or worse, whim) that we were not burned alive or minced with shrapnel, that evil was in fact the presiding god — this was the larger truth that could not be countenanced.

The external and the internal meet in an explosion of presence when a knife or a bullet enters flesh. The explosion is merely diminished, the injury more subtle, when the flesh is not your own. Chance divides the actual from the true.

The Actual (and I'll not dissemble again).

This is what happened: a month after the German plane destroyed our house, the same plane — or another — wasted more bombs on us, leaving our ruin complete. Cowering behind the Bogomil stones in the upper meadow, we survived. When night fell we began walking, carrying some bundles of salvaged possessions and two live chickens — Uncle, Aunt, four children, one dog.

We trudged through wrecked villages toward Bojnik, which we entered before dawn and found also in ruins. Some people were living in their smashed houses. There was little reason to stop except for rest. An old woman watched us from the empty frame of a window in her roofless house. Bloating animals — dogs, goats — lay here and there. Uncle asked the woman for water and she swore at us with forceless anger. We sat on a broken wall. Birds sang and the sun rose, throwing heat at us, promising a cruel day. There were explosions somewhere very far off, the sound ovoid, almost benign. Uncle had words with Aunt, and pronounced that the daylight was less dangerous than the night for travel.

We resumed walking, stopping near midday by a stream where we gulped water and built a fire, cooked and ate our first chicken. We drowsed, half-dead, then the sound of a tank and Garo's barking jerked me awake. The machine throbbed and clanked past us on the road, spewing black fumes. Uncle said it was Italian. We gathered our things and moved on, walking through the dust churned up into the still air. The road climbed into rough karst hills, leading us closer to my German lieutenant, and to the Drina River town of Višegrad. My aunt's people lived there, if they still lived. We hoped they would take us in.

Chapter Seven

JUNE 4, 1992
MANASTIR STRASTANICA

Dear Axel,

I hope you got my message at work re safe arrival. Didn't want to wake you at home. Three days now with the monks. It also took three days to get here — a little worse than expected, but now I'm settling in, immersed in the *new*. We could not fly into Belgrade, reasons unknown. Landed late at Niš with a flight out promised for morning, shuttle offered to nearest hotel. In the hotel bar I struck up a conversation with a fellow strandee, Derek, a British journalist who joined the flight in London. His second assignment to the war, first was Vukovar. He advised that flying back to Belgrade was pointless, I should enquire about a bus in the morning from Niš direct to Sandjak. We moved on to the current situation, what drew me here, etc. I told him about Pimm. He said I'd better hope my search for roots doesn't lead to Bosnia — which of course is obvious. When I mentioned Strastanica he started talking about Gregorian chant and I got to correct him:

Serbs have their own chants. Gregory was a Catholic. I got points with that. He'd slipped up. Then he had to get on top again. He told me Muslims had been forced out of Sandjak. I know this of course, and I underscored it by describing some of the local history. He knew quite a bit less than I did. Eventually he knocked back the last of his vodka and asked if I wanted to come up for a nightcap. I wondered if that meant he was available. But I've been out of commission so long. And I did need to sleep. He gave me his card, which had a handwritten phone number on the back for the Holiday Inn Sarajevo.

A tumble with Derek might have been interesting (he's thirty something and trim) but his nicotine cloud and general look of scruffy exhaustion left me iffy. I might have learned more about the Bosnian conflict. But he's a reporter, into the thick of it, and Sandjak is well out of that. There is clearly no chance of Bosnian Muslims attacking Serbia proper. Even within Bosnia they are outgunned and outmanned, and the embargo will keep them that way, which is outrageous. Does this compromise me? Would I be more admirable if I'd refused to lodge with holy men suffering under a national taint? I have a romantic idea of war-wounded being cared for by the monks. We did it for Pimm, and of course it's about as romantic as a car accident. But I had moments of complete calmness and even happiness, sitting by his bed at night, holding his hand, listening to his flutter of breath. I had momentarily forgotten what I was losing.

However, re transport, I did board a bus next morning for Pljevlja. The trip took all day. We seemed to stop every ten or twenty kilometres. Landscape increasingly rugged as we moved west. An assortment of people getting on and off: old men in wrinkled suits; mothers and babies; babushka women; a peasant couple with chickens in a crate, which despite protest was relegated to the luggage bin underneath; teenagers with radios and acid-wash jeans; four rosy-cheeked lads with knives in their belts, draped all over each other like puppies. The radios mixed rousing military tunes with pop songs. The lads sang along.

At Pljevlja spent the night in a hotel room reeking of cigarettes and disinfectant, with tired furniture from the sixties, rusty water in the pipes, drunks shouting in the street 'til dawn, sporadic gunshots. In the morning enquired about the noise, was told the U.N. had just imposed new economic sanctions on Serbia-Montenegro covering just about everything, which probably means I got one of the last commercial flights in. Breakfast of greasy eggs and boiled coffee; my waiter's guess was that bus to Priječko left twice weekly. I went out and walked the few blocks to the bus station. I passed a large and ancient-looking mosque. It looked intact but deserted. Weeds were coming up through the paving stones. The bus depot was a kiosk, closed. The post office nearby was open. That's when I phoned you, guessing that I'd have trouble doing it from the monastery.

The hotel helped me arrange an alternate way to Strastanica: in an old Fiat with squealing brakes on potholed roads climbing up stone hills with hairpin turns, no guardrails. The driver smelled like a brewery. He told me in Serbian and groping English what a fine fellow Milošević was. Priječko is a mostly Serb town, but on our approach he gestured smugly as we whizzed past some abandoned houses with their doors gaping, windows broken. "*Turčini*," he said: Turks. He waved goodbye over his shoulder. A jerk. My monks seem much nicer — and quieter.

Toni was right. Strastanica is beautiful: crags and cliffs, stony fields, pine and spruce on the slopes, oaks and willows in the river valley, big beech trees around the monastery itself. An extensive vegetable garden, small cornfield, sheep bleating outside my window, free-ranging chickens and geese, goats, a few cows with clanky old-fashioned bells. Nights are cool, days getting almost hot. I've been tramping through meadows and succumbing unexpectedly to two-hour naps. The air is a little thinner here. Abbot Nikolaj has given me a set of guest rules printed in Serbo-Croat, English, German, Greek and Italian. Strastanica used to host medieval scholars and retreat types in the summers, now there's only me. The monks themselves come from all over Serbia and Montenegro, Bosnia, Kosovo. More than twenty brothers here, but so far Abbot Nikolaj is the only one who has conversed with me beyond a greeting. His English is better than my Serbo-Croat. He gave me the tour, church and frescoes, garden, dining room, laundry etc., efficiently describing the histories and functions of things. He paused before an icon of Saint Sava and gravely noted that his bones had lain in a nearby church for centuries before they were stolen by invading Turks. Finally he led me up the hill to the guest building: eight small rooms, shared showers and toilets. His face is slightly lopsided, with the thick welt of an old scar running from one ear down to his Adam's apple. Probably an old operation, but I've imagined Ustashas with knives. He's old enough to have been a Partisan. Or a Chetnik. Or maybe a monk, even then. He seems mildly oppressed/depressed, I'm sure because their income has been unusually scant, for two seasons now — and, of course, there's the war next door.

Practical stuff: there is one phone line, and guests are not allowed long distance calls going out, which means I can't call unless I beg a ride down the mountain to Priječko and feed stacks of dinars into a faulty pay phone. You'll have to call here. Nikolaj suggested Saturday afternoons. If you call about 10 a.m. your time the monks are at prayers, so the line will be free. Took me 'til today to get laptop and printer speaking to each other, but now they're purring away. Your tech advice is responsible for these pages.

I'm on my way to the noon meal. Food is plain, satisfying. Fresh greens from the garden. Tomatoes, peppers and other healthy things yet to come. Meat and dairy are out on fast days. Maybe I'll go veggie.

Much love,

Chris

PS. JUNE 8

Sending this today. It's just past noon now, a week since arrival, my window open, breeze getting quite warm, a few grazing sheep painted on the far meadow. My mind is clearing, focus sharpening. This place will set me right again. The more I let the past recede and allow this new world to enter me, the more I can grasp Pimm's final impulse — the need to reinvent, to fend off decay. To not be defined by losses.

xoC

JUNE 18

Dear Axel,

I've been to the registry office, at the town hall in Priječko. They were not terribly excited by Pimm's birth certificate. A woman at the counter listened to my story, went into a rear office. A man, older, came out. He glanced at the certificate and said it could not have been issued at Priječko, because in May of 1945 the town was destroyed. He looked of an age to remember the destruction. I pointed to the top of the form where it said "Opština: Priječko." He picked up the form, brought it up close for a good squint, then put it back on the counter and spun it to face me. He placed his finger on the blurry rubber stamp at the bottom. "Rudačac," he said. Pimm was born at Priječko, registered at Rudačac. He gave a little shrug. Rudačac is in Bosnia. I found it on my map. It's close, actually closer to the monastery than Priječko if you cut straight across the hills. Regardless, if Pimm was born in Priječko then that's where my search has to begin. The old man said he had no records for any year before 1947. I asked if he could search 1947 and subsequent years for me, it might at least show the presence of Kožić families, possible connections. I told him I'd come from Canada for this. He wearily held my gaze. Did I want death and divorce along with marriage and birth? I did. He ordered the secretary away from her clack-clacking on a typewriter (the whole office is a throwback to the sixties.) They both disappeared. I waited. Up by the ceiling a photo of Tito regarded me with suspicion. The woman came back with a small stack of files, said she'd bring more as needed. She spent a few minutes showing me how to read them, then she directed me to a table and went back to her clacking. I got out my notebook and settled in. The Priječko opština includes the surrounding villages and rural region — nearly ten thousand people. I was there over six hours. I worked my way through to 1975 before I found a Kožić: Rajko, who married Ana. They had two babies. Through the stale air and cigarette smoke and the endless clack-clack I felt a surge of purpose. Then, a Ljubomir Kožić, died in 1982, at age seventy-one.

Likely the grandpa. Then the names disappeared. No more Kožićs, right through to April of this year. I'd already checked the district phone book: nothing. I asked the registry man if they might be unlisted. He seemed unable to grasp the question. Might there be an old address on file for Rajko Kožić? He smiled: "Are you a policeman?" I'd reached a wall. The simplest explanation is that Rajko and his family moved in for a few years, then moved away, and possibly not too far. He could be in the next district. More news as it comes.

Living with the monks can be a little eerie — even comical. Not only do they not speak to me, but some pretend not to see me at all, even at close range. Or they actively avoid me, turning corners when I appear. Yesterday there was a little breakthrough. I was on a bench in the garden, an elderly brother ignoring me while he did some weeding. On the gravel path I noticed what looked like a pair of fingernail clippers. When he moved off with his bucket of weeds he kicked the clips into the dirt. I couldn't leave them to rust, so I fetched them and rehearsed the Serbian for *Did you drop these in the garden?* He came back toward me, knelt down to more work. I moved in and held out the clips. He stared with a look of panic. He took them, thanked me in Serbian and English, and we both backed away bowing and smiling. It was the first truly spontaneous exchange I've had in these two weeks.

I'm outside their social loop. Without free talk there is no small talk, and all the encouraging tics that go with it. Talk makes wit, and charm, and maybe seduction. I'm aware that part of me wants to lift those black robes (selectively, mind) and see what's on offer — but nothing obviously is. Or else I haven't broken the code. I've read that in Orthodox monasticism celibacy is less important than obedience. What might *that* mean?

Mealtime provides the camaraderie. Two long oak tables seat twenty-one monks, two boys of about ten (twins, Bosnian war orphans), and me. A sideboard is set against windows that overlook the plum and pear orchard. Father Nikolaj heads one table and the retired former abbot, frail and dithery, the other. Nikolaj himself looks to be near seventy. My assigned seat is at the abbot's table, as distant from him as possible, which I think puts me not so much at the bottom of the hierarchy as completely apart from it. On a long diagonal opposite me is Brother Stefan, thirtyish, the choirmaster, who leads the brothers in plainsong and other chant — some of it quite elaborate and dissonant, completely new to my ears. The twins serve as sopranos when they're not in Priječko for required schooling. I asked the abbot about them yesterday. They are Brother Stefan's nephews, his sister's children. Their parents were killed this spring in Bosnia. A niece, the boys' sister, is sheltered with friends. Stefan is craggy handsome, with thick dark hair, a patrician nose, serious mouth. When the music is flowing over him his eyes soften and glow. His beard suggests a Christ-like goatee. He seems to be the resident artiste — he also authored the little guide to the icons and frescos. (I suppose it sounds like I'm smitten, but all this must be put against other bros who range up to one hundred and look mostly like unmade beds.) As we sit at table Stefan sometimes gives me an acknowledging look which has no real warmth, but a sort of knowingness, as if he's wise to something — my queer secret? The amount of my donation? Maybe both.

Meals are made by the brothers on a rotating schedule. They also make cheese and bread, wine (from trucked-in Montenegrin grapes) and plum brandy, doled out for special toasts before dinner. My first night, I was welcomed with a quick toast. I took a delicate sip and found myself the only one without an empty glass. Food doesn't vary much but I can hardly expect them to bounce from Provence to the Punjab like we do. Wednesdays and Fridays there's no meat or dairy, but I've found some of those meals more interesting (and digestible.) At breakfast yesterday had a delicious baked savoury pie thing layered with onions and peppers. I was starting to wonder where the Friday fish came from — discovered a stone dam across a stream ten minutes' hike up from the cemetery, behind it a large pond with trout flashing up from the depths. I've been told it holds two thousand fish, their numbers slowly growing despite sating twenty-three healthy appetites each Friday. The abbot perked up when I said I'd been to the pond. He's proud of his fish. (If only they would stop overcooking them.)

Eating in silence took some getting used to. Because eating is not silent. Mouths and gullets make noise. You realize the useful distraction that conversation provides at meals. The dining room sounds sometimes like a pack of spaniels chowing down on their Alpo. They do talk some, or rather interject isolated words of request or expedience. The point is to have no *idle* talk. But serious talk never happens at meals either. Food is the focus, eaten with unabashed zeal. The abbot signals the arrival of new courses. I've learned that if I dawdle, my soup will be snatched away in favour of getting the meat on site. No one sends anything back, but I've sometimes had the impulse. Liver is like hard rubber. I've seen Brother Stefan ignore a platter of dry porkchops in favour of more vegetables or dumplings. He's never shared a meeting of eyes with me over such things — that of course would be disloyal, and I'm imagining a connection that's really nothing more than my own fantasy. The house wine is adequate — plain and potent, served at supper only. Some brothers abstain. The others do not loosen appreciably except for the Old One, who falls asleep and makes little snucking-cacking noises until he's gently urged from his chair.

I'm starting to rise most days with the sun, which is too late for the monks, who begin devotions in their rooms at four. I do some exercise and a walkabout before breakfast, and find some others on the paths doing the same. No gym gear here. Basic black is it. I'm conspicuous in my nylon track pants (shorts are a no-no).

Later:

Just back from the church. Late sun is slanting in my window. Chant is drifting up the hill — Stefan still rehearsing with the brothers. I participated in the evening liturgy today. The abbot enquired to ensure I was baptized. I was able to join in the sung responses. The whole service is sung by Nikolaj, the chant choir and all participants. The music is completely present, ordinary and imperfect, and full of — it must be devotion. It's gentle and powerful. None of the cold precision found on CD. All of this is good for me.

I haven't mentioned the church frescoes: there are sections still pocked and broken from fifty-year-old war damage, other parts crumbling away simply with age. One wall was restored meticulously in the sixties and looks almost brand new — quite jarring. I stare at the pious faces, the gaudy robes and halos, the long insinuating fingers, and I think how smugly contented they look: *I've got a secret.* Like an abstracted expectant mama. (It wouldn't seem odd to see a watermelon bulge under the brocade.) I'm supposed to find beauty, and I do, but my mind leapfrogs to sacrilege — can't seem to give these saints the attention they demand. All that aside, the deterioration seems a terrible thing. The ceiling frescos are 13th and 14th century and they've got sections all but obliterated by water damage. There's a resurrected Christ in the dome with his face dripping stalactites. Maybe some of my cash will go into a restoration fund, though it seems to me they need it just to keep up with the ordinary decay.

I walk daily. Tomorrow morning I'll climb over a rocky hill and through pine woods, where a rough path leads to a cave without end, or rather an end I'm not brave enough to seek out. There's an old fire pit with some bones lying around (no skulls.) I'll bypass the cave and explore beyond.

Heading to supper now. Do you know when Toni will be back in these parts? I think she said something about Montenegro in August. I'll need a place (and a pagan) to escape to now and then. Do you have her new address on Riverside?

Much love,
Chris

Chapter Eight

JUNE 25

Dear Axel,
You may have phoned without success. When it rains there's a problem with wet wires — i.e. the long wire running down Jelenje Mountain.

Almost a month here. Toronto seems very far away. We've had two days without a sound from Bosnia. The war noises are not constant, but there's hardly a day without some far-off explosive sounds. A reminder: this all occurs in another country. I'm well outside the range of stray bombs. Some of the brothers follow war news on the radio. No sign of a TV here. Communal listening happens around a chintzy hi-fi console in the dining hall, but never during meals. I pick up very little from the broadcasts. I'm not listening, though I'm starting to feel I should. No doubt they're tuning in Bosnia radio as well. Propaganda fills the air.

Here's a lad to ponder: Jovan. Pronounced gently: "yah-vn." A boy of twenty from nearby Bučje, his left arm truncated halfway between wrist and elbow, dark hair spiky on top and buzzed off the sides, eyes like dark chocolate, a thick rendering of English words. He is mostly silent and massively present, like a Clydesdale. He delivers sides of beef and pork to Strastanica and to the hotel bar in Priječko, hoisting them onto his shoulder from the truck. His injury disables him as much as a hangnail. Like those boys in certain pool and casino bars in Dubrovnik, he is casually open to having his body worshipped by Westerners who self-define as gay, as long as they don't chirp too loudly. When he comes, he smiles like an angel through large pearly horse teeth.

Courtship: I was in the kitchen garden after breakfast, observing the progress of beets and turnips, etc., when Jovan drove up in his truck. So I got to nod and smile and watch him heave bloody carcasses onto his back while I did a little weeding. He wore over his shoulders a leather mantle that was caked with grease and blood. When he was done he discarded the mantle and produced a pack of Marlboros. He got up onto the hood of his truck and reclined against the windshield, stretched himself in the mid-morning sun. I kept weeding. When I glanced at him he was basking, watching me, smoking lazily. I said a few words to him about the beautiful morning. He looked at me through slits. I flicked a wrist at the sky: "The sun! The garden is happy!" He smoked. When I went past him with my weeds he caught my eye and gently cupped his crotch. (Am I so transparent?) I told him I needed a ride to Priječko.

He drove at the expected alarming speed, steering largely with his stump, pulled off the road onto a track between tall trees and down into a grassy hollow, a green bowl studded with white boulders. We got out of the truck. There was an odd hiatus, the sun throwing heat on our backs. We moved silently toward a stream rushing over stones. The sound of it seemed amplified. Jovan flicked his cigarette into the stream. I felt dizzy and imagined he might pull a knife and slit my throat, chop off my dick, the full Balkan horror show. Instead he put his hand on my behind. I didn't want that so I took the lead, turned to him and began kneading his pectorals, gently tugging his nipples. I told him to take his T-shirt off, which he did easily with his one hand. He was redolent, his pits like cut scallions. A furrow of black hair running between sculpted abs, circling his navel, pointing down into his jeans. I eased the zipper down and his cock sproinged out, uncut, hard, thickly veined. His balls big and loose. I decided against oral, just employed the magic fingers. His knob swelled to livid magenta and he grinned at the sky and shot ropes of béchamel into the air.

He had no interest in reciprocating. I went to rinse my hands in the stream. When I climbed back up the bank I couldn't see him. Some goats were descending the slope of the green bowl. As I came round the truck, there was Jovan with his pale buttocks angled over a white boulder, his pants down at his ankles. In the silence a faint crump of war from the north, clink of goat bells, burble of the stream. There was a smirk on Jovan's lips when he glanced at me. I looked away. The goats came down the slope and nosed the air. I got into the truck and waited, and as Jovan joined me an old man appeared on the hilltop with more goats. He shouted at us and Jovan shouted back, thrusting his stump out the window. He started the truck and drove us away at a lazy pace while the old man's voice harangued us, got lost in engine noise. Jovan was smiling, a thin smile, his teeth clamped.

You're likely thinking that I took a risk. Maybe. But please remember, dear concerned Axel, that you're not here and not quite in a position to judge. Jovan has the bias of all Serb patriots in these parts. The goatherd is Muslim. His Turkish goat-pies pollute Serbian soil. Jovan may have just been caught short, but I also think he was marking his patch of earth. He probably thinks I'm on his side, living with his holy men. I'm no threat at least. I'm an inconsequence from cushy Canada. And you, do consider this, you might well have succumbed to that meaty hand patting your bottom. You'd be biting the turf, clawing up divots.

Jovan has broken a long dry spell. I can't remember when I last stroked a stiffy that wasn't mine. He'll be back, of course, with his cargo of meat. I think I'll make myself scarce. I'd be miserable if the abbot ejected me for misconduct.

I keep wondering: what do these rough-hewn gents in black think about all day? The war, of course, and the whole Yugoslav convulsion, everything in flux. Aside from that is it simply God? They're men, not saints or angels. Brother Stefan is groomed rather than hewn — combs his hair, trims his beard, seems to wash regularly. But there are limits to hygiene here. Aside from the remote (and shunned) guest building there are only two washrooms with showers, so hosing down two dozen bodies before breakfast is impossible. In any case, it would play havoc with devotions. If I wake any time after 4:30, morning chants are wafting from the church. They leave me to drift back into peaceful sleep, usually, unless they're accompanied by the rumble of distant guns, which no one, by the way, ever refers to — at least not in my presence.

I'm getting hooked on the evening services. The chant choir is seductive, and it's clearly Stefan who keeps the fire going. The music they make sends me soaring sometimes. Tears come and I hide them with a bowed head, as if I were a believer. I really can't tell in these moments if I'm grieving or happy. It feels like both, all spiralling together. A little scary. When I sang with Pimm at

St Thomas's it didn't have quite this force. Suffering is supposed to nourish faith, but that mental gymnastic still eludes me. Here faith is meshed with the communal: meals, kitchen and garden duties and other chores of all sorts (called obediences and assigned by the abbot), and of course the liturgy, morning and night. Brother Lukijan has just come with the cart for my bedding. Sheets get washed today — every third Thursday. They don't waste soap and water.

I'm no longer in the motelish guest building. Maybe the abbot was feeling sorry for me, trudging through rainstorms to get to my dinner. Or maybe it was because I broached the question of fresco restoration and heard his story of churches burned in Bosnia and Croatia, and I'm now being courted as a benefactor. Last week Petko, the resident handyman, came knocking on my motel room door to say Nikolaj had arranged a room for me down the hill. He's put me at the end of a hallway, somewhat apart from the holy men but under the same roof. I don't know whether it's my dollars or my soul's need that decided it, and it doesn't matter. But it has crossed my mind that if I'm going to help restore churches I should really find some mosques to rebuild as well — it's all getting a bit out of my range.

Anyway, here I am, living with oaken doorways, wonky stone floors, windows like bottle glass, and bits of straw showing through the plaster. The room has a little electric heater mounted on an asbestos plate, with *Heat Wave* in Cyrillic across the grill. It doesn't work, but maybe that's seasonal. The abbot flips a hidden switch.

I wanted to thank Nikolaj, so I worked up a little speech in Serbian. I nabbed him after lunch and enthused about the new digs, said I was "honoured." I am.

I'm settled now to stay through October. Nikolaj is glad to have the extra two month's revenue, but the problem is how to get the funds to him in good time. I'm trying to set up a transfer from Toronto. Sanctions are not supposed to apply to foreigners but there are hoops that need jumping through.

So yes, I'm staying on awhile. You can see that my plans are in flux. I miss your voice, and your presence, but I can't say I miss that big empty house.

Tomorrow I'm going to look for Kožićs.

JUNE 26

I walked down to the valley road this morning and stuck my thumb out. The day was long. There are no evident Kožićs in Priboj. Pljevlja has two in the phone listings. I called them. They're one family, moved into the area from Vojvodina in the 1970s. Saša Kožić of Sandjak raised no memories in them. They told me their name is rare — not quite news at this point. Vojvodina's the other end of the country. I could expand my local search. Of course, local around here also means Bosnia.

I'm up and down about this. Part of it (this is hard) is that I've been waking up at night with thoughts that grow into a twisting misery. I just wish it would stop. It's still at me and now it's become this, this raging at Pimm in the dark. I have to get up and distract myself, go walking, look at the stars, which brings better thoughts. But it's all past past past. These feelings are nothing like the flow that washes from me in the church. I can't express it. I loved him too much. Dear Axel, you know.

What do I hope to find? Saša Kožić is dead. His history died on a refugee boat in the Adriatic. What's the point of telling his uncle or cousin or half-sister (*if* they exist, *if* I find them) that a man they never knew is now permanently unknowable? They'll give me a cup of coffee and nod at his picture, see or imagine a resemblance. Maybe I'll drink with them for a night. Then back to present dangers. If I did see Pimm's face appear in a doorway it would be striking, a flash of connection — but leading where? It's proximity that connects people, not blood or ancestry. Blood implies duty and security, but if anyone connects with anyone it's because of something else. People are alone and shared blood is no comfort and anyway I haven't shared blood ties with anyone since 1983, when that teenager in his muscle car mowed down my mother in her wheelchair outside St. Joseph's Hospital. The cancer was just settling in to do its work on her. Remember the night I rolled around on your carpet? Wailing. I couldn't stop. You and Pimm looked so stricken, helpless. But that drunken teenager was an angel of mercy. Instant oblivion. Pimm missed that chance.

Comfort is shared lives. Sometimes with a shared bed, but that's a perk. Pimm and I shared great sex for a year, the *issue* of sex for a few more, then ten years of chaste bliss. We never felt a need for separate beds or rooms. The deepest love, the tenderest caresses suffer nothing from being sexless. Now I'm welling up again and getting twisted again, like an old widow. Enough.

What happens here must be a renewal, a new life.

Love,

Chris

PS. JUNE 27

Don't know what I'm going to say if you phone, I think I've spilled the works already. I almost feel like we've been talking, which is absurd.

Tomorrow is Vidovdan. Feast of St. Prince Lazar and the 603rd anniversary of the Serbs' defeat at Kosovo. That's when the Turks (the real ones) moved in for five hundred years. Jovan sees them still, wandering with their goats, and he either fails or refuses to comprehend that their blood is as Yugo-Slavic as his own. Nikolaj showed me a framed photo of the crowd from the six hundredth anniversary, all assembled in front of the church. Tomorrow, priests from Priječko and Priboj and nuns from Banja arrive to join townspeople, farmers, soldiers, the whole local spectrum, for a special service. In the morning there will be baptisms in the stream at the bottom of the cemetery. (Our drinking water comes from a pipe further up, to avoid corpse leakage.) The twin boys, whose dead father, Stefan's brother-in-law, was Muslim, will be immersed in water laced with the runoff of dead Christians, and thereby brought into the Orthodox fold — too late, alas, to save their foreskins.

xoC

Chapter Nine

Dear Chris,

Got your first letter. A relief. And a treat too. Reminded me of the
ones you used to write from Amsterdam, the summers you were
there with Pimm, him flying in and out on his high finance biz
and leaving you to all that Gouda. You reveal so much in print.
You sound exhilarated. That's what we want, if you can sustain it
at the gates of hell. But I'm only reading last month's news.

I'll be in NYC this week for a doc on the U.N. Also seeing a gal
at NBC re career move, not a shoo-in exactly. Anyway, I'll take a
week's holiday, see Antonia. I'll send you a postcard. I phoned
yesterday, 10 a.m. as suggested, but it didn't go through. I'll try
from NY.

Do you get CNN or any English news? Last week 100,000 pro-
tested in Belgrade against Milošević. Dubrovnik has been shelled
twice since you left but no one's reporting it. Bosnia is the lead
most nights. I notice the Serb Orthodox Church has distanced
itself from Milošević. I hope your monks are in on that.

Your Brit scribe sounds like Derek Andover, who won awards for Belfast & Gulf War coverage, also reported from Vukovar. Sarajevo sounds like the right spot for him. Our handsome daddy Gen. McKenzie is moving his boys around Sara right now but it's just getting messier.

Toni's been calling for news about you. She teaches at Columbia in Sept. but late July and Aug. she'll be in Montenegro. So you could visit and maybe go lie on the beach like a sensible tourist.

Much love,

Axel

JULY 17/92

Mad One:

Photo on reverse is almost my Central Park view. I'm staying with Toshi and Bernard. They've moved up, 25th floor. Was at U.N. for taping Wed. morn. Antonia was great, did fab expert on 12 hrs. notice. Saw Bosnia's new seat. Yugo's is empty. Toshi's sculptor friend was gaybashed yesterday on Perry St., right on his doorstep. Is no place safe? They broke his jaw. No arrests yet.

xox A

On a hot Saturday afternoon I hovered within range of the communal phone, in the echoing entrance hall that links dining room, churchyard, residential wing and the abbot's office. Axel and I hadn't spoken for seven weeks, which was some sort of record. This time the ring came, just after 4:00.

"Toshi says 'hi.' He's making my breakfast. Did you get my letter?"

"Nothing yet. I guess you got my first."

"You mean there's more?"

"Oh yes."

"Are you a monk yet?"

"Hardly. Monks love Jesus. I think that rules me out."

"I hope no one's listening to this."

"They're still at vespers."

"Where?"

"4 p.m. prayers. Večernje."

"You're learning fast."

"I learned all that at St. Thomas's. I'm singing here too. Everything in the services is sung. The choir's actually very good."

"So, are you singing for Jesus or ..."

"It's for me. It's the communal thing. Just like at home really."

"I don't think so. You're in a monastery."

"It's not church all day. There's work to do. You know, life on the farm."

"How do you fill your evenings?"

"I write letters."

"What about the secret raptures?"

"They don't do that sort of thing."

"At all?"

"Not that I've seen."

"Okay. But is there maybe ... an aura? From anyone?"

"Maybe the choirmaster. But people join monasteries to get away from that."

"Not you."

"No. I did meet a local boy in fact."

"Meet?"

"The butcher's boy."

"Come on."

I told him about Jovan, checking the doorways for stray brothers. Then on to other news. Underneath it all, unbroached, was Pimm and the ancestral search. Axel inserted it casually. He might have been tired of waiting:

"Found any long-lost uncles?"

"There might be some in Vojvodina."

"Where's that?"

"Near Hungary."

I related what I'd found, which seemed more irrelevant as I told it. But I kept things upbeat. We moved on to the war. Axel had the facts ready.

"Do you know the Serbs are shelling Goražde?"

"We can hear it, if the wind is right."

"What do the Christian brothers think?"

"They're as depressed by it as anyone, probably more."

"Not as depressed as the Muslims."

"No, but does that make them guilty? Bombing people is not really part of monastic practice. Serbs have lost their homes too."

That left dead air between us. I asked about Toshi and Bernard. I knew Bernard had been ill in the spring. Axel said they were fine, but Toshi was likely still within earshot. We moved on. Toni had left town and would soon be in Montenegro — my plan to visit her in August was still on. He read me his postcard, then I made him promise to send it to me anyway. Before signing off he told me about Bernard. He was getting the purple blotches of Kaposi's sarcoma on his legs, also a new respiratory problem, so far undiagnosed. He'd started a new drug.

As we hovered near a close Axel mentioned an invitation to visit friends in Montreal in September, and I told him I was staying on at the monastery. He was silent, then tried to get a firm date out of me. I said November, aware that I was still waffling. I suggested he come and visit. I was hyping the rugged beauty of Strastanica when I heard a truck pull up outside.

The door banged open and uniformed men entered with a man on a stretcher. He was covered in blood. They wanted the abbot. They shouted it at me. The man was dying. I told Axel I was needed and left the receiver dangling, bumping the wall. I ran out through the yard and to the church. When I returned with Nikolaj a soldier was on the phone shouting in Serbian. Then he was dialling a number. The stretcher with the wounded man had been laid across two benches. The abbot sat on the bench beside the man's head. A teenager in a filthy uniform was crouched at his side. The dying man had only one leg. The other was completely gone, blood-soaked remains of trouser bunched against his pelvis. His entire midriff was swathed in crimson and brown-clotted bandages. A trail of blood came from his ear. His face was grey-white above his beard. He was young, maybe twenty. He looked dead, cold, but when the abbot laid a palm on his forehead his eyelids fluttered and his lips opened and he sucked in some air convulsively. The boy at his side stared at his face and repeated his name gently as if trying to wake him.

The older soldier was alternately listening and shouting on the phone. Outside the open door I could see other men in the back of the truck, some with the white of bandaged limbs. The man on the phone was long-bearded, supermacho, prominent knife and pistol and grenades slung at his belt — a Chetnik, the real thing.

He hung up and barked at the boy, they both crossed themselves and kissed the abbot's hand before leaving. The truck began moving as soon as they jumped aboard, spraying gravel as it spun a circle and jolted back down the drive.

The brothers began to come in from prayers. They gradually filled the room, crossing themselves, eyes staring or glancing away, heads bowing. I waited for Axel's return call. Nikolaj murmured quietly over the dying man. A smell was heavy in the warm room: sour sweat and fecal-urine decay, but not like the same smells from a sickroom — it was more like the slaughterhouse scent hanging in the air over St. Clair Avenue when I was a child.

Then the phone, Axel's tense voice, and my own. I told him a monk had fallen from a tree while picking pears. I'd helped carry him in. And the abbot had cut Axel off in order to phone for a doctor. Axel bought it. Two weeks later I told him the truth after he said July was too early to pick pears, especially in a mountain climate. He'd looked it up. His voice in that call was measured, remote. He was holding back a rant.

I hadn't told Axel the full truth. I'd already been introduced to war dead at Strastanica and had kept it out of the letters. A few weeks after my arrival I saw the abbot, in his black robe, standing at the bottom of the cemetery with a little scythe: the picture of Death doing the weeding, cutting away crabgrass from around a group of wooden crosses. I walked down the lumpy green hillside, through flat inscribed slabs and bulky stone crosses covering 500 year's worth of bones: monks, priests and bishops, victims of Ottoman and Hapsburg wars, all rearranged by Fascist bombs, then overlaid with fresh war dead, and even fresher. The four plain pine crosses showed names and dates in small metal letters pressed into the wood. On one grave was a tin box with a grated front and food placed inside. Nikolaj led me from cross to cross, his old man's eyes fixing on the names, reciting with resonance the ages of the dead. None had lived to thirty.

"This one was mutilated. No eyes." He looked at me and his lids closed.

The militiamen had come from fighting near Goražde. They'd been camped near the border town of Skovatići and a helicopter had fired grenades at them from the air. The dead soldier, Branko, was from the Bosnian town of Ustibar. He'd been baptized at Strastanica a few years before, with dozens of others, on the six hundredth anniversary of Vidovdan. Before he was taken from the vestibule I watched Brother Sergy, our nurse, inject him with morphine. The stretcher was carried out through the cloister to the infirmary. Robes fluttered at the clotted bandages. Branko died a few moments later. Nikolaj took his ID papers and went into the office. He would try to contact the family. If they couldn't be reached, he would be buried at Strastanica. So Branko was the fifth. Another pine cross.

I joined the monks the next afternoon for Branko's funeral service in the church, then his burial in a pine board coffin. Nikolaj poured wine onto the mounded earth. Fruit, bread and hard sausage were placed in a mesh box, to be refreshed as required for forty days while Branko's spirit seeped from the flesh. His comrades turned up a day later to take his ID and jewellery and pay their respects. From the kitchen porch I watched one of them light a cigarette, then twist it filter down into the loose earth. Branko would not be deprived of a last smoke. Brandy was splashed over the ground, then they each took a pull from the bottle before propping it next to the cross. They came up the hill.

As they passed the porch, the leader — the bearish long-bearded one — saw me pecking at my laptop and came over.

"Tanjug?" he asked. He'd pegged me as a journalist, and a Serb propagandist at that.

I said I was only writing a letter. I told him I was sorry for the loss of his friend. He opened his big hand and together we looked at a scuffed wristwatch, a thin gold chain, a signet ring with the image of a saint. The Chetnik's eyes were dry, his face closed. He would carry these items, he said, return them to Branko's parents. He asked if I was a Serb. I said yes, by marriage. He held my gaze for a moment, stepped back and flashed the three-fingered salute, *Serbia Forever!* and left before I could respond.

Chapter Ten

KOSOVO POLJE, 1989

Now we come to Blackbird Field, the place of dead dreams awakened. Here we succumb fully to the absurd and epical. My evil twin
is en route, imminent, whirling over mountains in his Valkyrian
war machine. Its blades hew chunks from the summer morning.
The fierce wind flaps Slobo's jowls, but is incapable of altering his
impeccable badger hair. He squints at rock and scrub, naked crags
and tumbling rivers, the sloping sheep meadows and ragged corn-
fields tended by overbreeding Albanian villagers. The Islamic peril!
A teeming assault on nature's balance! The pilot skims close over
red roofs, goats and horsecarts and tractors, barking dogs; he banks
and climbs over treed hillsides. The homeland. History will retrace
its arc and the circle will close. Slobo's eyes widen, viewing the
future; he will speak of it to thousands within the hour. He checks
his breast pocket for his notes. He touches his stiff bristle with a
gesture of anxious affection. No, it has not budged.

A million Serbs are gathered on the sacred ground of 1389,
the field of defeat. Here our glorious Lazar was murdered by

Ottoman devils. The crowd surges and heaves in the sun, seeking the god from the machine, the god who will transform oppression into ecstacy. O history! O wondrous loss! O mythic perfect injustice! Men and women weep and grow faint with anticipation. Six hundred tragic years! Turks, Croats, Austro-Hungarians, Germans and Italians, others — all had their turn, all grinned as they desecrated our Princes' graves, devoured our women and cattle, our corn and potatoes, guzzled our stores of wine and brandy, then copiously shat upon the ruins. Then came Tito, staggered by the weight of his living legend. He drove out the Fascists and gave us peace and a famous whispered refrain: OZNA *sve dozna*, the secret police find out everything. And then came English lessons. And German lessons. And tourists. And, yes, prosperity. A life of comfort built upon quicksand. And a miracle: the rats in our house became our brothers! More shit. A country cobbled from patches of foreign soil that never ceased to pollute the sacred earth of our fathers.

The living saviour arrives with the dead one and his priestly handlers. Saint Prince Lazar is returned! Admittedly somewhat ossified, a relic, truncated and adulterated by several centuries of enforced travel. Pieces of him occasionally fell off the cart. Others were perhaps stolen by special admirers. No matter. Real-enough bones prop up the jeweled vestments beneath the sealed glass cover of his gilded casket. The skull is intact. Beneath the looming stone tower of the Monument to the Heroes of Kosovo, the people file past Lazar's coffin, noting the sheen of the rayon lining, kissing the glass, fingering it with sweaty hands. Some linger and must be pulled away. A bishop is posted with consecrated spray cleaner and a towel.

But Freedom Man is now descending! He is landing on the field itself. The bone dust of martyrs flies up. The crowd shudders and gapes. As one, they surge toward the great plummeting Russian bird, their frenzy reflected in the mirrored sunglasses of twenty bearish men in black suits whose air of legitimate threat holds the crowd magically at bay. Slobo's chariot touches earth. Other men in black suits, older and fatter, are instantly disgorged from the chopper's belly. They expertly scan the area, then post themselves at the open hatch. The President himself emerges. He stands beaming. The tails of his Italian suit dance in the blade wash. He acknowledges the bellowing crowd with a single raised hand and the ancient tripartite salute, a gesture of consummate assurance and dignity. His chin points at the horizon. His gaze shoots down the bridge of his nose to meet the glistening eyes of his people. They chant, "Slo-bo! Slo-bo!" And something else, a rhyme, "O Prince Lazar, here is your shining star, Slo-bo, Slo-bo, marching at your side!"

Cordoned by security, he makes his way through assembled officials, black-robed Metropolitans and scuttling media persons, past breathless costumed folk dancers, to the dais. He mounts the steps, glances at his notes, then looks up, radiating proud benevolence. He waits for silence to envelope the multitude, waits until the only sound is the faint flutter and snap of a hundred identical flags in the breeze that softly caresses the patina of sweat on his cheeks. Then the chin thrusts ever so slightly forward: "My celestial people!" he begins. The crowd releases a seismic roar.

Zlata and I battled these pilgrims to reach Priština. Zlata, my daughter, who possibly resides now in Skopje with her husband, but the war has intervened and I'm uncertain. On this day of

Serbian National Convulsion we were beset by private sorrows. We arose early and set out from Zlata's house in Medvedja. Our destination was the Priština hospital where my wife had successfully killed herself some weeks before, jumping from the fifth floor window of an equipment room that rightfully should have been locked. My Hana had been plagued with darkness since the death of our son Marko in 1985 near his JNA training base. Marko's was a stupid, puerile death, and also extremely Yugoslav — indeed, Zlata laid her brother's death directly at the feet of Tito's dream. Serb and Croat and Muslim recruits had gotten drunk together on leave, and, while returning to base, had competed in a test of bravery on a railway trestle.

The morning of June 28, 1989, we sat motionless on the highway outside Priština in my daughter's car, a blue Yugo. Before us and behind us were other Yugos and Fićas in fading primary colours, fuming tractors, trucks and buses, horse carts, Volkswagens, some nicer German cars for the well-heeled. A vile belch and swelter in the midmorning sun. Sometimes we stuttered forward. The walking poor easily outpaced us. A fly buzzed idiotically in a corner of the windshield. Without warning, I fell to pieces. A month without tears and now a snivelling flood. I hid my face.

Zlata looked at me, wisps of dark hair clinging in the sweat on her neck. She had cried from the moment of the terrible phone call. She had cried cooking dinners and eating them, her tears salting the meat. As she sorted books at the town library her eyes were swollen red. Later that same afternoon in the hospital office she would cry with touching extravagance. But now in the car she looked at me, peevish, and said, "What happened, tata? What's wrong?" I snuffled and shrugged. I wiped snot with the back of my hand. She returned her gaze to the farting bus in front of us and leaned her palm on the horn, which inspired others, and a dinning chorus arose.

The hospital psychiatrist was also late to our meeting. He obliquely referred to "this madness." He had an Albanian name. He offered us coffee, motioned us ahead of him into his office. He settled himself and angling his head in sympathy, read to us from his report, translating Hana's blackness, the vacuum she had entered, into clinical terms. He assured us that the offending key-holder of the fatal storeroom had been fired. Zlata cried and I didn't. I listened, nodded. I thought: this little lapse has ensured Hana's peace.

In the barracks of Tito's Yugoslav National Army our Marko drew a veil across his Muslim maternity and called himself a blood Serb. His intact foreskin allowed a simple identity. My paternal family were Serb farmers. In 1921 my young father, Davor, was sent to buy a sow in Jajce market and stopped to hover at the fringes of a Communist rally. A day later he returned to sign up. Defying his parents, he attended a party congress in Sarajevo, and there he met Šafrana. They lived for the cause and in sin; no church or mosque would marry them. A few years on, the Communists banned and everywhere persecuted, they escaped the city for a calmer life. Šafrana made a show of conversion and they were wed in a church. My parents' home became a few acres of land near Sjecišta, not so far from Uncle Vaso's. Vedrana was born. Then came little Slobo. Then we were made orphans in the war with Fascism.

Serb-Muslim Slobodan married Muslim Hana. Zlata was born, then doomed Marko. I wanted to retain my Serbness; I decreed that Marko would not have his penis cut. Zlata grew up and went to the university, abandoned a brief flirtation with strict Muslim orthodoxy, met and married a Serb student in Belgrade and moved with him to the town of Medvedja. He is reportedly one-quarter Macedonian and one-eighth Bulgarian. I remember a map and a chart of genealogy framed in Zlata and Srdjan's kitchen. I stared at it one day when I was there alone, at the table drinking brandy, considering family and the past, how it happened that there came to be a Slobodan Kušić drinking his son-in-law's slivovitz in a place called Medvedja. The map was carefully, lovingly hand-drawn. Red dots on certain towns. Refugee trails. The chart bracketed family names recast in foreign phonetics. New homes. Marriages and children. People connected equally by blood or its irrelevance. Beyond the edge of the page, unknowable cousins whom one might meet some day in battle or across the till of a market stall. Ancestors who, if they'd been known, might best have been avoided at all cost.

TRADITION

On the bridge over the Drina at Višegrad were performed recurrent impalings. The practice entered world consciousness measurably in 1961, when our famed novelist, Ivo Andrić, won a Nobel Prize, in part for not shrinking from the worst.

Impaling is an exacting skill. The state of impalement, on the other hand, requires no skill whatsoever, insists only on the common physical attributes of an anus and the spaces between vital organs. Vital organs are the impaler's great challenge. With great delicacy, in increments achieved by precise blows from a mallet, he advances his sharpened stake through the internal spaces, leaving only two scars on the ungrateful impalee's body: one the pierced rectum, the other an exit wound in the upper back above the shoulder blade. The metal-tipped point, once free of the lower bowel, nudges and nestles carefully past loops of intestine, stomach, liver, kidneys, arteries, slips through the diaphragm alongside the esophagus, moves up behind lungs and heart, and with a final expert blow pierces muscle and skin to pop out of the shoulder. Death is certain, but not quite imminent. The impalee has time to ponder his predicament. To avoid corporeal slippage, the pole is fixed at a certain angle with a wooden chock. The twisting occupant, or surroundant (for the pole is the occupant), is thus conveniently placed to observe the taunts of the populace, and to reply if able. To impale and to be impaled, are each, in quite different ways, a union of the fleeting actual and the eternal true.

A man is on a pole over the Drina in the late Middle Ages. He is still a man: his eyes blink, breath sucks in and out, a soft moan escapes him at intervals, though he seems unable to reply to taunts. His feet are flat on the smooth stones of the bridge's central span, for he has slipped some distance down his angled pole. His arms hang stiffly out from his body as if poised to break a fall to earth that never happens. He seems three-legged, a malformed man-pole hybrid creature. One absurd wooden leg grows straight and firm from his behind. He appears to stand on his gangly man's legs, bent slightly forward, while the pole leg serves as a useful lean-to, pointing through him like an axis toward the heavens. He is naked. There is a small crowd: peasant serfs, women out to their marketing, town burghers strolling, the exchange of neighbourly wit and outrage. The central *kapija* of the bridge is cantilevered over the waters, a broad space with stone benches where citizens and travellers linger and observe the panorama of town, the changing sky, the waters rushing down from the hills. Today some avoid the bridge, while others are drawn by novelty, fascination, gleeful contempt. The spectacle of the pierced is welcome: fully just and thus freely enjoyed.

The impaled Serb is said to have stolen a child, raped her and crushed her skull with a rock. This is possibly true. The punishment is undeniably true, stunning, marvellous and necessary. The child's parents have come to throw rocks at the Serb. The father has been restrained from slitting the man's throat, which would be an unconsidered mercy. Children are fascinated by the event. They come close, to examine the intersection of stake and buttock. It is a rude joke. They move quickly from awed silence to a sprightly aggression. Some boys lash the Serb's behind with willow branches. Then he dies, following a ragged, inspiring rattle, and much spitting of gore, after which the bereaved father steps forward to slit with a flourish the lifeless throat. He stands, his face a knot of miserable triumph, watching the dead spill of blood. The dazzling crimson brilliance. An ancient sweetness stirs in his heart, gaining ground in the fight against repulsion.

Chapter Eleven

"There. You can see minaret. It is white." I stood at Stefan's shoulder, sighting along his arm toward a distant hill. I could see a small stripe of white against the green.

"That is mosque at Rudačac. Church is also near, but you cannot see." He stepped away from me without shifting his gaze from the view. "We sang there, few times, these past years."

We'd hiked for almost an hour, past the meadows and up through slopes of oak and maple, then along a winding path rising through conifer forest to the edge of a sheer cliff. Far below, a sea of woodland rolled away to the Bosnian border. On the way up we'd exchanged hardly a word.

Stefan had found me that morning in the dining hall with a map spread over the sideboard — a detailed German map, showing even peasant trails leading to villages beyond the dirt roads. He came over and stood at a brotherly remove.

"Good map. You are going some other place?"

"I'd like to go to Rudačac."

"Very close, but I think this is not wise."

"No. Or possible."

"Is possible, but not good idea for you." He moved a little nearer, then stretched to place a slender finger not far from Sarajevo. "Here is my birth home. Sokolac."

"Your nephews are from there?"

"No. From Zvornik." His finger slid to Bosnia's eastern border.

"I was very sorry to hear about your sister."

Stefan kept his eyes on the map.

"Here, little south from town, is their house. Maybe boys will go back there after the war. Or maybe stay here. I don't know."

His English was better than the abbot's. I asked where he learned it and he shrugged, "In the school. English and Russian. Your family is from Rudačac?"

"Possibly Rudačac. Somewhere in this area."

"Parents?"

I told him I was researching the roots of an adopted brother — the same lie I'd given Nikolaj in my initial letter. Then Stefan offered to show me Rudačac. There was time before lunch, he said, if we went right away.

At the lookout there was a crude bench: heavy, weather-worn planks with their ends set into piles of stones. We both seemed to understand that resting there together was not on the agenda. But I did take a moment to examine what was carved on the planks. Serb and Muslim names abutted and overlayed each other. Stefan drew my attention back to the horizon. Together we watched a column of black smoke slowly billowing from behind a ridge. He moved off down the path.

"Come. We cannot miss the meal."

On the way back, breaking a silence, I asked how long he'd been at Strastanica.

"Six years."

"Where did you study?"

"Belgrade. I have degree in music of course. Then seminary. Chris, you have seen our lake?"

"The trout pond?"

"We will pass by, to look at water level." He picked up the pace.

I'd hoped he might open up a little, maybe reveal a life before the cloister. At the pond, he was more forthcoming about Nikolaj's background. I wanted to know about the disfiguring scar.

"Wartime. After war he became the priest."

"He was a soldier?"

"He was Partisan, with Tito. He is telling this always to novices. He was teenage soldier, Communist, but war turned him back to God." Stefan smiled slightly to himself. "Truth is that he was cut by Chetnik knife." He looked at me. "You know what is Chetnik?"

"Serb Royalist."

"Yes."

"Or nationalist. Like Karadžić."

"Yes. You know."

"He's destroying Sarajevo."

Stefan's brows lifted at this. He looked for a long moment into the pond water. "Karadžić is murderer. He also has help from Izetbegović and mujahadin."

"Are there really mujahadin in Bosnia?"

"You doubt? Chris, Arabs are in Bosnia, and Afghans, and Turks, fighting beside Muslim soldiers. Do you know, there are

Serbs still living in Sarajevo? In their houses and their apartments. I know them. They do not want this war. They are dying beside Muslims and Croats. May God save us from our leaders." Stefan stared past me. With his eyes shining, he turned and walked out along the narrow wall of the dam, then bent to pull a length of rope from the water. He slid a plastic clothespin a little higher, marking the level.

I climbed often to the lookout after that, but not joined by Stefan. For days afterward he barely acknowledged me, which intrigued me all the more because his attitude wasn't indifference. We'd broached the question of Serb guilt and settled it by blaming warlords and fanatics, avoiding harder, more dismaying questions. Any hope of a solution, it seemed, came from God.

There was another reason for his standoffishness — a more promising one. It was settled when I hung a second too long by his shoulder at the clifftop. The air between us hummed. When he moved away it was like magnets tugged from each other's fields. Now I was sure about Stefan.

But I gladly spent time on the clifftop alone. The long view pulled me out of myself. Early in the morning the sun would sometimes pick out the domes of Rudačac's Orthodox church, and always there was the pointed white stripe of the minaret, helping me to think the town's Muslims would be spared. By October the minaret had disappeared.

I couldn't remain apart. Branko's death, the killing of Stefan's sister and her husband, the orphaned boys raising their fragile sopranos in the church, it was all inseparable from the monastery and its threatened peace. A perfect morning could bring a pine coffin through the gates, trailed by wailing women, stone-faced old men and teenagers with guns.

And there was the media war, crackling from the hi-fi in the dining hall. Some monks showed little interest. Some had portable radios in their rooms. The abbot scheduled radio use in the dining room. Communal listening happened daily between vespers and supper, or before bedtime. The evening cut-off time was generally 6:30, when the abbot took his place at table. I'd begun listening in on some of the broadcasts. The standard fare was either RTS Prijepolje or Radio Pale, from the Bosnian Serb headquarters outside Sarajevo.

One night a larger than usual group was huddled around the hi-fi. Pale was airing an interview with Karadžić. The monks bent their heads trying to catch meaning through the static. Others, Stefan included, were already standing by their chairs when Nikolaj shot into the room. He cut through the brothers, switched off the broadcast and hustled to his chair, and was already crossing himself as the monks moved to their places. He waited with head bowed. When he had silence he recited the usual prayer, then abandoned Church Slavonic for regular Serbian. Stefan gave me an ironic glance. Nikolaj went on. His message was simple. He was praying for honourable leaders, a stop to the killing, mercy for the victims.

Later Stefan said, "Abbot has no regard for this propaganda. There is need for information, but from Pale and from Muslim radio, very much is lies. Also from Belgrade. And from CNN too, different lies, more money."

Radio Pale was second fiddle to RTS. I'd seen its outrageous propaganda on screens in Niš and Pljevlja, and in Čeko's café bar in Priječko: *Radio-Televizija Srbije,* spreading Belgrade's hysterical manipulation of images from a century of Balkan carnage.

Chapter Twelve

First week of August, I went to visit Toni. She was in Nikšić, three hours away. Her older sister Jelena lived alone, a divorcee, her kids grown-up and gone. She and Toni welcomed me with a generous meal, over which I learned that Jelena's son was in the military — a source of worry more than pride. It occurred to me that he might have bombed Dubrovnik, but the question was unaskable.

Toni seemed pleased that I'd hit it off with the monks, and even that I was planning a longer stay. She wasn't at all surprised that I was bogged down with the Pimm search. She suggested I might hire professionals — after the war.

I was kept busy. Toni was doing field work for her book on Montenegrin blood feuds. We zig-zagged up mountain roads to hamlets of stone and timber cottages. Many of the houses were abandoned. Later we visited Ostrog Monastery, its church famously clinging to a wall of rock midway up a cliff. People were lined up to fill soda bottles with holy water dribbling from a pipe. I practised my Serbian with a nun herding the pilgrims, told her I was a guest at Strastanica. That got us a snack in the kitchen pantry: bean soup and a platter of room-temperature pork.

I saw Toni again before her return to New York. We spent a day in the Mt. Durmitor preserve, then went on to Podgorica, the Montenegrin capital. I'd been weighing the idea of a car and she knew of one that would be coming available from a colleague who was moving to England. The paperwork proved complicated; registration required residency. Nikolaj was the saviour. He agreed to sponsor me for religious study status — a slight stretch, but he had plans for the vehicle. Two months later I put cash down for a vw Golf. The car, and the residency card that came with it, were the measure of my desire to stay.

Abbot quickly assigned an obedience. On Monday mornings, I was to drive Stefan to Priboj, where he'd begun giving weekly music lessons at the primary school. While he taught, I'd do a little shopping for packaged goods or garden supplies or whatever else was rendered in Cyrillic scrawl on Abbot's list.

My second obedience arrived with a knock at my door one November morning. I opened up to see Stefan's face, his trim beard and measured smile.

"*Dobro jutro*, Chris."

"Stefan. *Dobro jutro. Drago mi je da te vidim.*"

I gamely rattled on, inviting him in, saying I rarely had a visitor. He hovered in the doorway and answered in English.

"Okay. This is not for visit but more for information. I have news from Abbot. He is ready to give new obedience. Not in garden, but you may continue with this for pleasure, of course. It is for church. Abbot is enjoying your voice in liturgy. So, I made suggestion for him. You will join chant choir. We need more, what is your English word, middle voice ..."

"Baritone."

"Exact. The baritone will help us."

"I would be delighted."

A flash of smile, "And we also. It is new music, practise for the Christmas."

"What is the new music?"

"Rachmaninoff *Vespers*. I have rescored for nine voices, and boys, of course."

"Stefan, I'm honoured. It's a beautiful piece."

"So. We will start today, after service."

Stefan offered his hand, we shook. When he leaned in to give me the kiss — cheek, cheek, cheek — he seemed suddenly flustered. A waft of nervous sweat rose to me through the cloth of his cassock. I felt a surge of response but he was already gone, receding down the dark hallway with his robe swirling behind him.

Music, especially sung by monks, is leashed passion. At rehearsals some of the brothers were standoffish at first. They had a new rival for Stefan's affections. But they were fine singers and knew it — I was no musical threat. We rehearsed four times a week after the regular vespers. Stefan worked us hard.

Chapter Thirteen

NOVEMBER 17, 1992

Dear Axel,

Your call about Bernard is still rattling around in my head. It wasn't unexpected. But we still don't know how to expect these things. I sent Toshi a note. I feel I know what he's facing. But you can't compare.

I had dinner in Priječko last night with a fellow named Vukan. He comes through now and then selling electronics and black market stuff — videos, cigarettes. He's been trying to sell computers to the monks, to Čeko, to anyone who'll give him half a minute. Most of the equipment is used. Nikolaj, after some haggling, bought a fax machine from him. Maybe I'll be granted occasional use. But do we want him reading your replies? I like real letters, sealed and delivered.

Now that the snow is coming I get to Čeko's less often. It's not the sort of place for a steady diet and the noise can be intrusive, but I like an infusion of beer or brandy now and then. It's my nostalgia for our out-on-the-town nights. Wine with the bros is two glasses max with dinner before things are cleared away. I have a bottle of slivovitz in my room, the cheap firewater sold everywhere, but it sits idle at the bottom of the cupboard. I like a clear head for the mornings. I drink less here than any of us used to.

But with Vuk last night I got rather drunk. He paid for us both from a wad of Deutschmarks. Vuk is a charming, vaguely scary con man. His patter sounds American but with that lovely liquid Slav English. I can't say we're friends, because he seems incapable of sincerity, but it's bracing to spend a few hours with him. He's fascinated by New York City but pretends savvy indifference. We drink and he patters on with his promises of rare and forbidden goods of "absolute best" quality and "price for to kill your sister even if she is virgin in convent," and incredible schemes for turning inflation into huge profit. Economic chaos is Vuk's paradise. He seems to think New York is the biggest and shiniest obscene profit machine ever. I tell him my own stories of Manhattan, feeding him detailed scenes from defunct gay baths and sex clubs, shamelessly substituting male-female relations for the homo ones. This is when Vuk shuts up and just stares blearily, balefully at me, and I can see the unattainable orgiastic visions roiling through his head. Then we get into his mud-spattered Mercedes and roar off down the valley road. He tells me filthy jokes, waving his hands around while passing farmers' wagons on blind corners. We turn off on a narrow trail and when we're well away from the highway he stops and shuts off the engine, puts my hand in his lap, and his goes to mine, and we wank each other for a bit, then he takes a condom from the glove box and we get out of the car and I let him ravish me against the fender. I'd prefer the back seat but it's full of merchandise.

None of that last part happened. He's a guy, the real thing. His unsated lust for women is like a vapour around him. But I did tell him those New York stories in the bar. His face went slack. He told me unlikely things about his nympho girlfriend in Užice. With Vuk I drop my good little boy gentility and pretend I'm a rogue. He really is a rogue. But he just wants to strike it rich and clear out to NYC, leave this place behind. He's full of deceits, self and otherwise, but no evident malice.

I did give in to another ride with Jovan, and it was fun, but it's a little chilly now for outdoor romps. There's always spring thaw. You know that Pimm had a taste for rough trade. I stuck to occasional encounters on fresh sheets in tidy apartments, with polite hellos and goodbyes and showers all round. I guess I was hungering for the rogues too. The Serbian outback broadens the mind. Then I go back to choir practice and no one's the wiser.

But I'm not going gaga about God. The impulse is there, yes. But God, the idea, is my antagonist. The world is rudderless. I've felt this since I was a child. We haven't talked openly about these things but I think you agree. It's a world of generous, breathtaking, miraculous gifts, snatched away. Bernard was one of the gifts.

xoC

Chapter Fourteen

The music carried me to my first January Christmas. The day of the concert I found the stones of the church floor covered with straw, its musty barnyard scent mingling with the smell of hot beeswax in the cool air. Church became stable, a reminder of humble beginnings. It made the crèche at St. Thomas's, with its dusty plaster figures and hay bales pulled from storage, seem like department store window dressing.

We sang the full Rachmaninoff cycle to a packed church, repeating it for dawn and evening services Christmas Day. The *Vespers* is otherworldly, rising in pulsing waves of sound. It filled the vaulted space like legions of ghosts returned to lament the long, tragic arc of Slav history. In the context of the war, the effect was close to grief, but mixed with enormous comfort. Then we feasted: roast pork, mutton, cheese and spinach pie, casseroled potatoes and peppers, and a table filled with cakes and pastries from parish women. Nikolaj estimated we had almost two hundred in the dining room and at folding tables in the entrance hall. People beamed greetings to the polite Canadian but seemed mostly indifferent to news of my Pr;iečko ancestry.

Winter brought its share of reduced comforts. It was often impossible for us to get out by car or for the truck from Priječko to bring in supplies. Mealtime lost some of its lustre. We had our fish, if the pond ice would support fishers. Otherwise, legumes were our available protein. We lived for weeks on bean, onion and tomato stews, boiled potatoes, cabbage and turnips. My garden duty turned to shifts of barn work: keeping sheep, goats, chickens and our two cows supplied with hay and grain, and relatively clear of their scat.

The night chill didn't alter my usual longings. Stefan and I had no reason to be alone together. The closest we came was sitting on the old couch next to the fireplace in the dining hall, where sometimes we'd hum our way through a new piece of sheet music or work quietly at passages that proved tricky in rehearsal. Here one night he told me about his time in Hilandar Monastery, on the Greek peninsula of Athos. It was where he'd learned the practice of Orthodox chant. His memories of the place seemed to give him spiritual rushes. He took on a sort of glow when he talked about it, meeting my gaze unguardedly. He needed me to know. But his eyes were focused on something well beyond me. In one of these sessions by the fire I told him what the chanting sometimes brought on for me, a welling up of sensations and emotion, warmth, a mingling of sorrow and joy, thankfulness and, most eerily, a sense of my self rushing out from me — of my personness, my singularity, dissipating into the vaulted space of the church. He observed me quietly when I said these things, his head nodding in measured recognition. It was the singing itself, the work in rehearsals, that made him give passionately and freely, but from a safe distance.

My musical confession to Stefan was the turning point. I finally admitted to myself the possibility that I had a hidden life, something mysterious and worth exploring, something more than just a love of singing and a need for simplicity and escape. I became a peculiar ersatz monk, different in kind but contained by the rituals. My voice, my obedience and (I have no doubt) my money made my halfwayism an easy fault for Nikolaj to overlook.

Chapter Fifteen

We had new music to rehearse for Easter. Days were filled with duties and pleasures all overlapped. The snow besieged us. To leave it all seemed impossible and unthinkable. As spring approached I saw the anniversary of my arrival rushing to meet me, and with it the fear that Nikolaj would give me an ultimatum: commit or move on. I waited, and waited, and got no summons to the abbot's office. I heard from Stefan that Nikolaj had remarked one day after service that I sang "like a believer." The weeks went by. In July, after my second Vidovdan and well past the one-year mark, Nikolaj called me in for an interview. He settled behind his desk and pensively shifted stacks of books and papers. He took a phone call, a lively chat about the electric bill, like he was trading barbs with an old friend. He hung up and considered me in a long silence, rolling the knotted beads of his *brojanice* between thumb and forefinger.

"You are an asset to our monastery," he said in measured Serbian. "You have done fine work. God's work." Stefan had praised my contribution to the choir. "Now you have serious questions to consider." He paused and looked at me squarely. "Do you believe Christ is your Lord and Saviour?"

I lied to him without hesitation. "Sometimes," I said. Then I told the truth. That I'd lost the person I'd most loved, and that I saw the same losses and worse everywhere and was doubtful that a loving God would allow this sort of random, unchecked misery. I went on with my little drama of suppressed emotion, part of me surprised at hearing it all come out in my terse bursts of Serbian, with hardly a stumble.

Nikolaj stared at me with weary eyes. "This is your argument for faith, not against it."

He heaved himself out of his chair and turned to a shelf of books behind the desk. He selected two, gave them to me to look over while he wrote down the titles. They were by Patriarch Pavle, aged head of worldwide Serbian Orthodoxy. I would find them in the monastery library. I was advised to pray, even if the words stuck, and to study these books and the daily liturgy. That was all. I was free to carry on. He suggested no date for reassessment.

I came out of the office clutching the Pavle titles, and when I went out into the cloister, there was Stefan. He turned and without a word we fell in walking, Stefan a little behind me, across the churchyard, along the rose path and through the kitchen garden. When I reached the bench overlooking the cemetery slope, I stopped. I felt in a daze, and sat down on the bench. Stefan remained standing.

"May I see?" He eased Abbot's scrap of notepaper from my fingers.

"He's letting me stay."

"These are good writings. I have some other also, if you wish."

He handed the paper back to me and I looked up at him:

"You were a factor, an influence. I'm grateful."

"You are also influence on Abbot."

"But I'm furious at God, at the whole idea. I told him so."

"You are not special for this. Belief is private, between God and one person."

Nikolaj would let me stay and not believe. But I'd equivocated with him on belief. I'd let him think there was hope for me, though I wasn't sure of it myself.

"Stefan, when your sister ..."

I didn't know how to finish it. He stared off down the slope, his face unreadable.

"Cousin also was killed. Yes. Thirty-four years. First month of war. He was forced on work detail in Sarajevo. He was digging trenches."

I knew Stefan had other family still in Bosnia; he'd been scant with details. He moved to me and sat, the length of bench between us.

"Where are your parents now?"

"Ilijaš. Close to Sarajevo, but there is not fighting. I think they are safe. I hope."

"How do you pray about these things?"

His eyes held on me, then shifted slightly.

"It is difficult, of course. We think there is no answer. But you know there is some answer, some reason. Maybe when you are singing and praying. That is God."

"Maybe it's just us. All inside us."

"God is inside us. We find Him there."

"Is He a Him?"

"Him and she, these are human words. God is outside human."

"You said He was inside."

"He is everywhere. Jesus was human and God." He shrugged. "Mystery."

"A big one."

"Big, yes. And a man is very small."

He stood up.

"Come. There is time for walking. And we will make a delivery."

We stopped in the kitchen and Stefan wrapped up some cold meat and put it in a grocery bag with a loaf of bread. We went off down the trail following the stream, passed through the village of Zabrdje, and then farther on to a patch of sloped meadowland and some scattered low houses. Some of the homes were overgrown, with broken windows, some just ruins. We stopped at a house and Stefan called from the doorstep. A voice beckoned us in. The old woman was in her kitchen over a bucket, washing the mud off some potatoes. She and Stefan greeted each other and she dried her hands and offered us tea, but Stefan said we had to be on our way. A little small talk, some admiring words about her modest plot of vegetables, then we were off. Our parcel of food, never referred to, was left on the kitchen table.

On the way back, Stefan took me along a different route, past a lead-roofed structure on a hillside that had the look of a small church, but with a misplaced, silo-like steeple. It was a mosque, Stefan told me, and three hundred years old. The woman we'd visited was Muslim. Zabrdje, Stefan said, had been a mixed village until the Muslim exodus spurred by the prospect of war, but was now almost entirely Serb, some of them refugees from Bosnia. They were among the churchgoers we saw on Sundays and feast days. The Muslim old folks still left, he said, were the ones too frail or stubborn to leave, and were without support.

In Zabrdje we stopped at another house and accepted coffee and packaged cookies. This house was full of women and children who seemed pleased to entertain a handsome, black-robed holy man. RTS was at a discreet volume on the TV but I seemed to be the only one watching it. Footage of a political rally gave way to a re-creation of medieval serfdom. People toiled in the fields, horses pulled wagonloads of corn. Then peasants and livestock were on an epic march led by sword-wielding men on horseback.

We arrived home in the nick of time for vespers. I sang and bowed my head and, conscious of Abbot's knowledge of my doubts, refrained from accepting the broken bread said to be the Body of Christ. The Blood could be taken only with advance fasting and special blessings. As I watched the several who'd elected to take wine that day, I wondered if I would ever be ready. I couldn't see how any of it embodied any real God — not in my rational mind. But the irrational was everywhere around us. Maybe faith was a reasonable leap.

The routines and the familiar departures from them — funerals, weddings, Saints' days, choir visits to nearby parishes — had the effect of blurring events into a continuous present. I felt cradled in it. The monks were becoming family — much like my original family: present, dependable, predictable, never truly known. Čeko's café bar in Priječko remained my secular escape, and yet I could feel lonely there, even in the midst of distraction by Vuk or the television or the lads bellowing soldiers' songs or love songs or querying me, with a strange mix of bravado and deference, on what I was doing in their little corner of Serbia and why I'd bothered to learn their tongue. I was the strange Canadian who lived with the monks. When I came in Čeko would say, "Welcome, Father!" Vuk and the boys would laugh, "Here's the peacekeeper!" All of which left me undefinable. Holy men could be respected; two of our monks had brothers soldiering in Bosnia. But peace-keepers were a joke.

I never saw a real monk in Čeko's, and Nikolaj never betrayed concern over my evening drives down the mountain. Stefan, once or twice, suggested I was straying, but he didn't harp. Outside of duties and prayers, monks have their private time. We might be in our rooms or in the barn or halfway over the mountain. I kept secrets as easily as any brother. There are no confessionals in Serbian churches. Sins are admitted to God alone, or to no one.

Chapter Sixteen

Charged with delivering Nikolaj to Morača Monastery, I arranged to go on to Podgorica for an overnight visit. Antonia had taken a small apartment there, giving her a research base for her upcoming sabbatical. Meanwhile, she had a new project drawing her attention. A journalist friend in Sarajevo for the *New York Times*, Martin Ivry, had asked her to translate a Bosnian refugee story. Sitting in her spartan one bedroom I read the first few pages: eyeballs in a basket, Rambo Chetniks, Muslims terrorized on a railway platform, all of it written by a man with no eyes and no thumbs, who also happened to be dead.

"Is there more?"

"Not in English — but soon."

"Who is Slobodan Kušić? Is he alive?"

"Apparently."

"With thumbs?"

"I don't know."

"Eyes?"

"Well, let's hope."

That, and the fact that Kušić was in Sarajevo, was all she could tell me.

"I thought it might interest you — wasn't Pimm a Kušić?"

"Kožić."

"Ah. *Izvinite.*"

"*Ne mari.* But it does interest me."

"I'll send you more. I've got another twenty pages."

That June, Toni paid a visit to Strastanica. She had finally accepted my long-standing invitation, agreeing to a two-day stopover on her way from Nikšić to Užice. On the day she was due I put myself to work in the kitchen garden where I could keep one eye on the road. The warm day stretched on. It was five before her Land Rover growled up the pebbled drive. When I went down to the gate to greet her she was assessing a dime-sized crater in her windshield.

"I've had rocks and dust flying at me all the way from Pljevlja. Troop carriers, heading north."

"Better rocks than bullets."

"True." She gave me an appraising look. "You've got a farmer's tan. And an even-more-priestly beard."

"Anything to confess?"

"I wish. I don't suppose they drink here?"

"Wine with dinner, or a little brandy."

"Unlimited?"

"Hardly."

"Maybe we should eat in the town."

"That would be better. I know a place. We can talk."

"Of course, monks don't do that. Talk."

"Only if necessary."

"How about 'I'd like a gin and tonic'?"

"Nope."

"I brought you something, a case of Italian red."

"A case?"

"You can share it. It's my Uncle Teo's, from his Refosco vineyard."

"Thank you, Toni, what a treat."

"It won't disappoint. I need a bath. Can I leave my vehicle here?"

"Around the back. It'll have to be a shower — unless you want to soak in the cow trough."

She threw me a glance and got back into the Rover.

Toni had the temper of the road on her — the troop carrier dust. I wondered if she'd been delaying her visit to Strastanica to avoid a brush with the border zone. She would have known it was a training ground for Serb militias. To grind through the mountains of western Sandjak and see Chetnik slogans painting empty houses, it must have brought things home.

I made sure we got to Čeko's early, before the TV and the boys got too cranked up. As we ate I could see the bitterness in her, for all the expected things: the endless brutality, the pussyfooting of peacemakers, the reduction of Serbs everywhere to symbols of crude vengeance with scant hope of redemption. Having finished off her dessicated chicken, she ignored her fried potato in favour of a cigarette. She inhaled deeply, coldly assessing the TV screen.

"None of it matters. The gut response, I mean. Tortures, drunken rampages, herding people off cliffs ... Yes, it's astounding and horrible and must be stopped. Yes, we feel sick. We are angry. Emotion emotion emotion. It excoriates the mind. I avoid feeling. It drains me of useful response. Feeling outrage — it's finally a wallow. Diplomats wallow consummately. They're pros. We want analysis. Not bluster. Uninvolvement — there's something to analyze. How do you interpret a head severed by a blowtorch? We watch, then turn to something less ghastly, less demanding. We must think, not feel. Uninvolvement is something you can ponder. Yes?"

"Yes. Do you want another drink?"

"Of course."

She drained her apricot brandy. I ordered her a refill and myself another beer. Behind her, papering the entranceway to the bar, was a grainy floor-to-ceiling photo blowup, peeling at the edges: a generic Marlboro Man on a white horse, swaddled in a sheepskin coat, backdropped by crags and snowy pines, a shotgun crooked in his arm. He was the only decorative accent in the room, aside from two Serbian flags crossed high on the wall behind the bar — most likely in the spot where Tito used to hang.

Toni stubbed out her cigarette.

"The usual agendas here invoke history. What history supplies, or fails to, gets reconstructed as avenging myth. Myth and memory. It all goes into the same greasy casserole that festers before it can nourish, and then everyone is poisoned. My father used to make a traditional *djuveč*. You've had it surely."

"Every other Saturday."

"Utterly disgusting."

"I like it."

"You never ate my father's. He made it because my mother refused. Ground meat, rice, potatoes, fried eggplant, cheese, peppers, hunks of pork fat, all cooked to death and then baked in a clay pot. I loathed it, threw up on the table one night after he made me eat it. He had it weekends for lunch by himself, for years, when we were growing up in Novi Sad, an homage to his childhood in Požega — which I will drive through on Wednesday, by the way. Without stopping."

"Did you hate your father?"

"No. His quirks drove me crazy."

"He couldn't cook."

"Not for love or cigarettes. But it was other things. He was not an uncivilized man, but he had a fierce — very defensive — nostalgia for certain things Serbian, which comes partly from marrying an overbearing Italian. Mama can cook. I'll make you an Istrian feast some day. But Tata, rest his soul, took perfectly good ingredients and made an unholy mess of them. His pork *djuveč* is an emblem of his own history."

"Your history."

"Only half. I never really felt like a Serb. It's generational. My friends were Yugos, we didn't care what people were. By the time I was an adult with a real job I felt more like an American — well, a New Yorker."

"How did your father die?"

"A plugged aorta."

"Italian food is unhealthy too."

"Not as. But vengeance — no shortage. Italians and Serbs know about payback. This war takes me back to stuff I heard in the schoolyard, or when my father talked about the war, the big war. He was about the same age as Slobo Kušić, if not quite as ... expressive. Did you get the new pages?"

"They're beside my bed."

"That helps you sleep?"

"I wake up at night and reread it."

"You have a taste for blood."

"I ... it's the extremity of it. I think of Pimm's parents. The German planes. Running from the Ustashas. It's horrible, but it's thrilling too. I want to know if they make it, what happens in Višegrad."

"I hate to think."

"It's not too far from here."

"Višegrad? It's in Bosnia."

"I know that."

"Not exactly a weekend getaway."

The night crowd was starting to drift into the bar. I watched Čeko reach up to fiddle with the TV controls. An image of Homer Simpson flashed by with Cyrillic subtitles.

"Is Kušić from Sarajevo?"

"Not from. He ended up there, in the main hospital — what's left of it. Psychiatric wing. A strange man. And resilient. He's typing with eight fingers. Lost one thumb when he was a child and the other last year in Bosnia. He's using an Olivetti portable, started in January, a few weeks after they brought him in half-frozen. They found him living in a wrecked truck near the airport. It's a wonder he wasn't used for target practice. Spends all day typing. He writes more than he talks. The staff treasure him. Thank God they care. They call him a compulsive — but lucid, as we know. Really, he seems to me no more compulsive than most writers. I get installments by satellite from Martin, through the *Times* — when they're able. They're on generator power part of the time, if they can even get the fuel. Martin's doing heroic work there. He's working on a three-part story about Kušić for the *Times*."

Toni squinted at me through the smoke of a fresh cigarette.

"You realize you look like the fucking Patriarch with that beard. All you need is that big golden hat. What happened to our drinks?"

I looked around for Čeko and saw him greeting a youth in combat fatigues. A few more straggled in and clustered at the bar. They were almost certainly from the training base in an old auto-parts warehouse outside town, fresh from a day of war games: teenage village boys rehearsing the assurance and swagger of warriors. Čeko attended to their need for brandy. He joined them in a toast to Serbia, another to Montenegro, then he left the bottle. Toni observed this with me, then picked up her bag.

"Let's go before they start singing. Or fighting."

She left twenty Deutschmarks on the table.

"Toni, let me get it."

"It's okay."

"You've left too much."

"Never mind."

Under the first stars in the dusky June sky we crossed the broken asphalt to her Land Rover. I turned to Toni's shadowed face.

"I've sung with them, on occasion."

She stared at me in astonishment.

"What? Why?"

"They're from the region. Militia."

"They'll be burning houses. Raping and ... you know that."

"They could be dying with their balls cut off."

"Yes. But things are not equal."

"I've been here two years, Toni."

"What does that mean? You're a Chetnik apologist?"

"Boys come of age and they get put in uniforms."

"Muslim boys too, except they don't get enough weapons."

"They don't all choose it. They'd rather be rock stars or ... teachers, poets, some of them."

"Are there such boys here?"

"The kid wiping tables inside. Čeko's son."

"Chris, teenagers are not blank slates. You're such a romantic. Do you have to sing with them?"

"I've done it maybe twice, drinking with Vukan. 'Serbia Forever.' What do you want them to sing, the 'Internationale'?"

She fixed me with a stare.

"Who is Vukan?"

"He comes through with black market stuff."

"Grenade launchers."

"Fake Marlboros, porn tapes — he sold a fax machine to the abbot."

"Are you friends?"

"Hardly. We've had drinks now and then. He shoots off these incredible lies. And monologues of swearing — I mean beautifully constructed swearing. Like jazz riffs."

"Like a bullet in the head."

"It's all a con. Totally mercenary and totally charming."

"You're not flirting with him I hope."

"All the boys flirt with each other here. It's subconscious."

"Best to keep it that way."

She climbed into the Rover and I got in beside her. We sat quietly for a moment.

"How old is the boy in there?"

"Old enough. His pals are putting the pressure on. Madam Čeko's already crying for him."

A car arrived with more soldiers, rough-housing as they entered the bar. Toni's face hardened.

"They should keep the hell out. Bosnia's a sovereign nation. They're violating an international border."

"What border? It's all Serbs with guns — from here to the border and all the way to Pale."

There was laughter from Čeko's, shouts for more slivovitz. Toni started the engine. We drove in silence. At one switchback the headlights swept across some ruined suitcases, clumps of rotting clothing. There was a damp, sweetish smell in the rushing air. Toni geared down for the climb to Strastanica and pitched her voice above the engine.

"It's a blessing my father died before he saw this. Before we saw it together. We would've fought like tigers."

We parked the Rover beside the guest building. Before she got out Toni turned to me: "Why don't we sample that red?"

"*Imate li vadičep?*"

"Yes I have a corkscrew. You almost sound like a real Serb now, if you don't blather on too much."

"I couldn't possibly blather in Serbian. Gibberish, yes."

Toni's room in the guest quarters was identical to the seven others in the low stucco building. It was like a charmless American motel room from the sixties. A framed print of St. Sava was the only devotional note. An orange plastic light fixture hung from a cord. Toni kicked off her shoes and propped herself on the single bed. I sat in the only chair.

"To guilt and honour. When my book is finished, I'm going to spend the rest of my days between Central Park and Riverside. This place is going to be hell for the rest of my working life."

"What about your mum?"

"She doesn't need me. She's gone back to her sisters in Trieste. Serbia was something she endured for her husband. She'll outlive me. This mattress is like a bad road — a very narrow bad road."

"Mine is no better."

"That's a comfort. How do they accommodate couples here?"

"There's a sort of Murphy bed in the closet."

"Ah. Farce potential."

"I slept in one once. A hotel in New York, the '64 World's Fair. I was ten."

"That makes you forty. Soon isn't it?"

"August fifth."

"I'll be in New York. Why don't you come visit? Take a break."

"Leave this for New York in August?"

"Think of the food. Theatre. Gay bars."

"Not interested — it all feels like a previous life. I'm safer here."

"That can't be true. Well ... possibly."

We drank from squat tumblers. A drift of night air from the open door was starting to ease the stale heat of the room. We talked about New York, her move at eighteen from Novi Sad to live with Italian cousins in Brooklyn, riding the train into Manhattan to study at NYU, returning to summer with her family in Dalmatia or Istria. Then she moved to the Village, shuttling up to Columbia for graduate studies. I mentioned my trips to New York with Pimm in the seventies, staying with Toshi on West 4th. We realized that we might have passed each other on the street or bought hash from the same dealer in Washington Square. The bottle gradually emptied and Toni slid further into the bed, nestling her wine between breasts that spilled softly over her ribs under the soft cotton top she'd put on for dinner. Breasts are the female parts that entrance me. I wondered if an offer was implied. But all that would have been far too big a challenge. I poured her the final half inch.

"Did you bring any more Slobo?"

"Some."

"Maybe I'll look at it tonight."

"In my bag there, the side pocket."

We drank up and said our goodnights, kissing like Mafiosi.

Chapter Seventeen

Rain brought relief from the heat, but cast a new curse. Other cruelties remained unchanged, keeping pace with our progress through ruined villages and towns held by Italians who ignored us, or by Ustashas who could ignore or as easily murder us if they were bored or drunk enough. Our destination was Višegrad, yet another several days' hike.

Trudging through steady drizzle along a mud-clogged road, Uncle exclaimed yet again how near we were to Višegrad, even as a hacking cough drowned his words. Aunt called him a fool. He flashed his yellow teeth, windmilled his arms to rally us forward — a ludicrous jollity. Aunt stopped walking. She stood staring down into the mud. She looked up and glared at Uncle still shuffling ahead, now pumping his scarecrow arms like pistons on a locomotive.

"Vaso!"

He halted.

"Vaso, the rain is not going to stop! So we must stop!" She scanned the roadside: sodden vegetation, scrubby trees, burned houses, and ahead on the right a house well abused but unscorched, with a roof. She marched past Uncle, veered off the road, picked her way through litter and smashed furniture to its gaping front door, peered inside. She shouted a greeting into the shadows. We waited on the road. When she entered the house my sister looked at us, then followed her. They appeared at a broken window.

"Come and look. It's not so bad. It's dry at least."

Uncle pondered the horizon. He coughed and spat green mucus into the mud. He approached the house and entered. So we were sheltered, suddenly and absurdly cheered by our fortune.

Uncle made his patriarch's inspection, Aunt already looking for a broom, my sister stepping over broken glass to open cupboards. I and my cousins followed Uncle from room to room, everything a musty chaos, not one object where it belonged. Strewn clothing, bedding, furniture, papers and photographs, a leather-bound Koran torn apart, floorboards ripped up, holes punched through plaster, pillows slashed open, walls splattered with bullet holes, a mattress crusted with dried blood, blood on the wall above it, and sprayed across the ceiling. Uncle closed a door on the blood. We went into the kitchen, Aunt now sweeping debris, my sister going out the back door with a bucket.

"There's a rain barrel, Uncle."

He said we would leave first thing next morning. Aunt gazed levelly at him and put her broom aside.

"Help me move this table."

There was scrapwood under the back steps. Uncle kindled a fire in the kitchen stove, and we dried our clothes. We still had some smoked salt fish from home, a quarter-round of hard cheese, one tin of meat. In the cellar we found some whithered potatoes, two jars of onions in brine, some mouldy sausage that we trimmed and fed to Garo.

The rain stopped. Uncle went down to a pond behind the house with hook and line and came back without fish, but in his hat some raspberries, which he divided into four little piles on the enamelled tabletop that Aunt had wiped clean. I remember Uncle's calloused fingers stained red, and the red blotches on the white enamel, the sweet tang of the fruit. We boys gobbled ours, but my sister said they tasted like dog piss. She spat into the sink and Uncle ate her berries in an indignant gulp. Closing our minds to the pitiful things all around us, we ate in the cramped kitchen, filled our stomachs with boiled potatoes, Uncle's smoked fish, briny slices of onion. Garo, as usual, ate our fish heads. The cheese and meat we saved.

A truck drove past at dusk. At a distance it slowed and turned, came back and stopped in the road, disgorged three men: an Ustasha officer in high, polished boots like Mussolini's, and two soldiers in clean uniforms. In the yard we were inspected and deemed mildy amusing, and more certainly repellant (disgust being, for a trampled enemy, the only possible variant of pity). I watched a soldier slap Uncle repeatedly about the ears until Aunt blurted that there was indeed a weapon in the house. She offered to get it, but the shiny boots posed and demurred and chose me instead. The two soldiers followed me inside and I pointed to the bag containing Uncle's rusty pistol, a relic from the Great War. (A war triggered, of course, by a Serb nationalist. Nothing can ever quite redeem us.) The soldiers searched the rest of our baggage, peered into a few cupboards. Everything they looked upon seemed to confirm in them the correctness of their contempt.

So they took our gun and left Uncle with aching ears, Aunt and my sister weeping, my cousin of nine saying, as if planning a tea party, that he would kill all the Croats some day, and roast them on spits and feed them to their mothers in a soup. Aunt barked at him between sobs for this last part. But it was just a schoolyard story (though not quite apocryphal), something mothers have heard and still hear.

We rested as best we could on a patch of floor, and began walking before dawn under stars in a clear sky. The sun climbed over a ridge and dappled us through tree boughs, and I felt that this day might be better. In Čežnjavica, Italian soldiers and Croats were camped in the abandoned houses. The main street was scattered with rubble, some civilians gathering it into piles while bored soldiers stood about smoking. A crazy woman in a dress caked with filth performed a bizarre dance, jerking like a puppet in front of the soldiers. They smoked and stared at her with dumb contempt as she lifted her dress to flash her pubis at them. Aunt saw the display too late, then hustled us past. Uncle later bartered his aluminum pocket comb to a soldier for some cigarettes.

As we left the town a hellish stench made us gasp and wretch. We passed a horse with legs stiff in the air, its exploded belly swarming with vermin. My sister vomited on the road, then so did my two cousins, and Aunt fussed, wiping their faces, because they'd lost their breakfast of cold potato.

We passed into the German zone. The cruelty of the Ustashas and the indifference of the Italians gave way to a measured suspicion. We were questioned at certain crossings, though never impeded for long. The day advanced. The sun stayed with us and grew too hot. There were others on the road, some with horse and wagon, some with wagon only, pushing and pulling, some lugging bags and suitcases. Some were clearly Muslim by their dress. Others, like us, attempted a non-identity. No one spoke; eyes glanced away. We were all closed inside our fear and exhaustion. Approaching a village at dusk we found an empty house, but it was so strewn with filth and debris that we slept under trees in the yard. The night was mild and dry and we were undisturbed.

The next day, on a narrow ravine road following a river, a Muslim holy man with horse and wagon overtook us. He was singing to himself — or it seemed almost to the horse. A mournful serenade. The man was fat, too fat for war's deprivation, a grizzled, sweating moonface under his white turban. We moved aside to allow his passage and he stopped his song to call a greeting, then he addressed his horse, told it to halt. After sharper commands it did at last halt, the wagon now well past us. The man twisted his bulk around to look at us. He asked our destination and sputtered at the response, "Višegrad? Forget it! Ustashas have taken it." He could take us to Žepa if that would do. We climbed into the wagon, six of us and the dog, a jumble of aching limbs and baggage. Uncle sat in front with our Samaritan. He was the *hodža* of Žepa's mosque.

We bumped along, spreading goodwill, working to get past the need to confirm it. The horse would fart now and then with ripping-sputtering sounds. "Poor Lijepota. She ate apples, rotten ones." We repeated, "Poor horse," and gazed with trepidation at her rolling behind.

Presented with these evidently benign Others, the *hodža* revealed, as if casually, the existence of Others among his friends, spoke of his young nephew, a communist, whose Serb wife was a nurse trapped in Višegrad, forced by the Ustashas to bandage the wounds of soldiers who would go back into the hills to fire upon her husband. He related all of this gazing far ahead at the road, with little anglings of his head, as if caught between black mirth and a settling despair, a despair that is simply submission before the unalterable.

The *hodža*'s words established alliances without firmly declaring them, and allowed Uncle to confirm, also indirectly, that we too had no love for the Croat henchmen of Mussolini and Hitler; Aunt's cousins in Višegrad were after all at their mercy, and what's more, my Muslim mother and her neighbour had disappeared while traversing a road between villages in the first month of the war. In truth it was probably Chetniks who had taken them, but in the *hodža's* wagon Aunt and Uncle allowed the implication to stand: that Ustashas had murdered my mother. It enabled us to freely share our Serbness and Muslimness with this kind man, and all to share equally our relief that this passage together to Žepa would not be soured by any evidence of Croat blood or sympathy. That my parents' village had once had its Croat shopkeepers, its Croat family on the hillside, who allowed us to collect spring water from behind their house, that the foundation of this house was built of stones given from my father's meadow, that Serb and Croat men had drunk home-brewed brandy together late into the night sitting on those freshly mortared stones — none of this mattered in the holy man's wagon. It was all an unspeakable truth buried safely under our careful language of survival.

So, the darker vision: This Slobo, who is I, this Slobo whose freedom is to write his own justifying auto-history, is, like any other

Slobo, reduced by a world teetering on suspicion and lies. My black self shrugs, having ascertained the worst: history is an exchange of distrust and devolving guilt that never tallies, never adds up to more than a cycle of opportunism and moral idiocy, a storm brewing always in the roiling clouds of money and politics, releasing the winds of destruction again and again upon the hapless. This is so everywhere and always, and alters only in the frequency and degree of chaos wrought. For we South Slavs the result is easily stated: every thirty or fifty years, we each start again from zero on a meagre plot of someone else's land, after powermongers and useful madmen have first compelled us to desecrate it.

And yet, as if to mock us, a semblance of good cheer settled upon our wagon. Things were, for a time, better. (Do tyrants ever feel such unaccountable gaiety? Is it what they seek, or is it something utterly beyond them?) A cool breeze flowed from the river gorge, making the sun feel less like a burden than a caress. Aunt was encouraged to cease worrying for her unreachable cousins in Višegrad (whom she hadn't seen for twenty years.) Uncle played the fool until she slapped his hand and he snatched it away, miming a child's face of crocodile tears; Aunt shook her head, her mouth set, but Uncle had won. She opened our food cache and said we should have our dinner as long as we were idle, and our kind *hodža* would certainly enjoy a bit of cheese or fish, perhaps some pickled onion? Uncle voiced regret that we had no brandy. "But maybe you don't partake, Mullah?"

"Ah, but I do," said the *hodža*. He instructed me to look under my seat, and there beneath a canvas was a crate of old soda bottles filled with clear liquid and sealed with wax stoppers. Aunt played indifference to Uncle's ceremonious opening of the bottle. The men passed the liquor between them, and Aunt, uncharacteristically, accepted the mullah's offer of a sip, just one, taken with a twitch of defiance.

We reached Žepa in the early evening, the mullah cooing gently to his horse, which was exhausted by the gruelling climbs and perilous descents that made up Žepa's natural fortification. As we rounded a bend entering the town, the road widened and at a distance stood the mosque: a low lead-roofed dome, and beside it the pointed white rocket of the minaret. To my child's eyes, minarets were rockets. I would imagine standing on the little ring of balcony near the top and soaring off into the heavens. I had seen a film when we stayed once at my grandmother's in Sarajevo: men travelling in rockets and visiting costumed people on other planets, Buck Rogers mouthing Belgrade Serbian. So we slowly approached this Muslim starship, and a line of shadow climbed it as the sun dropped behind a mountain. The town was quiet, sleepy even, the houses undamaged. Two soldiers with rifles slung, knives at their belts, came out of a house, and when they saw the mullah they stopped, bowed low, and received a prayer as we passed.

Now we stood stiff-limbed in the dust of the road, looking up at the calm sad moonface.

"I cannot offer you shelter. My own house and the mosque are beyond full. You can see."

There was indeed a crowd of people in the yard of the mosque, the smoke of cooking fires rising amid the bent backs of women, children running or dawdling, old men clustered on a low wall like birds, smoking, nodding, rheumy-eyed. Some of them glanced at us with disinterest or a vague disdain. Our attire in no way marked us, leaving open the option of weary contempt for whatever we might be. The mullah knew as we did that a mosque encamped by Muslims was not the place for us. His gestures of regret were both good manners and a mime for those who watched and hoped we would not be allowed to join the throng. He directed us to an abandoned feedmill a short distance down the street, and there we settled for the night with a half-dozen Serb families who shifted their belongings to give us room on the grain-scattered floorboards.

Žepa was within the German zone, but it remained a haven. So ringed was it with mountains and entrenched Muslim forces that neither Germans, Chetniks nor Partisans had managed to secure the town. Its Muslims and few Serbs had so far been spared the worst conflicts, left to muddle through the lesser ones spurred by the war's tide of forced nomads. The feedmill in Žepa was our home until November.

FEBRUARY 1994

Fugues overcome me. In the middle of the day I half-dream, half-remember. My nurses say I shout and laugh, or argue, or cry for help.

Now I am in the poisoned well, dead. A blessing! Death brings a certain buoyancy. In the documented manner I rise from my broken flesh, looking down upon its sad jumble. I hear the bereaved Rambos of General Izgorević high above me, performing their rituals of manly bravado, hefting without fear the machinery of battle, hurling angry lead at sparrows and rabbits without a flinch in their carved superhero faces. I float from the well and sit lightly upon the head of the one whose hopeful parents named him Spaso, the Saviour. I imagine depositing a soft turd on the top of

his head and cannot suppress a hearty laugh. He drops his cigarette and scratches fiercely at his scalp. His hand passes through
my ghostly pelvis — a soft tickle. Am I feeling his flesh or his
wasting soul? Flexing my new and untried powers, I form my
wisping ether to his body. I infuse him, and discover his flesh
to be salty, meaty, knotted and coiled. His mind is like broken
glass whirling. He then resumes wasting bullets. Perhaps sensing
my presence he points his automatic weapon into the well and
kills me again. But my body is now no more a part of me than the
foul water in which it lies. Spaso's bullets explode the misplaced
heroic eyeballs of General Izgorević, force them to mingle with
the nerve-pudding that once ruled the hapless life form known as
Slobodan Kušić.

I began to follow these bad boys. Like a doppelgänger, I dogged
them all the way to Vukovar. They drank plundered brandy, they
sang for freedom and they wept for it, they pissed on Catholic
churches and Croat graves and fresh corpses, swearing on the
pudenda of mothers. They honoured a boyish warrior tradition,
using heads as footballs. (A strange thing, heads as footballs. They
are too heavy. They do not roll or bounce. They gain no altitude.
They mess one's boot. The game lasts only minutes and is abandoned in profound disgust, yet new heads are inevitably supplied
and the ritual repeated.)

Spaso is the leader. He is twenty-three. He values his aging
Kalashnikov like a first born. His ammo clips are Bulgarian. They
sometimes jam the Soviet machinery. His sunglasses are Armani
fakes. His underwear is from a factory near Kraljevo, where his
grandmother works part-time and gets faulty goods at half price.
He has never screwed a woman with affection. He has only done
it with swagger and badly, or with the ritual cruelty of the warrior.

He hasn't bathed in two months; he mentions this often, like a threat.

I watch Spaso now, after the capture of two Croat miltiamen hiding in a barn near Osijek. Spaso's men mock the Croats' weapons: old hunting rifles. The two are beaten with these rifles, which are then fired close to their ears. Spaso orders a bleeding Croat to eat shit from a tin plate. The Croat will not comply until Spaso shoots the other Croat for not eating shit. Then the shit is consumed, but not completely, and Spaso must therefore shoot the first Croat too.

Some days later Spaso squats behind a bush for relief, and following a sudden helpless impulse he tastes his own waste, a tiny dab on his fingertip. He wants to see how bad it is. It's foul, but not as bad as he expected. Not the worst thing he can imagine. Is it worse to eat your own or that of your enemy? Should he have made the Croat eat Serb shit? Dog shit? Corpse shit?

Coming out of the bushes he is suddenly buffeted by a fit of loathing. His men stink like pigs. He orders them to bathe with him in a river, a tributary of the blessed Sava. But they must again don their filthy uniforms. Spaso alone has clean underwear, pristine in its plastic wrapper. He stands shivering and naked on the riverbank, balancing on one leg, pulling on his fresh white pants. He feels a fleeting anger that he has already muddied them. His men are laughing.

Chapter Eighteen

JULY 3, 1994

Dear Toni,

Slobodan has his claws in me. It hurts sometimes, but mostly it's a general, exhilarating hurt. He allows no limits, which seems to me pretty much the way God runs his stunning creation — or the way we run it (the part we can control), still hoping our saviour will drop in and tidy things up. The monks are good on this. Everything here, every devotion, works from the initial premise that the world is a fucked up miracle. They know the wonder and the deep hurt. What they don't have is my continuing doubt about Christ's redemptive powers, not to mention his alleged monopoly on souls — all of which I keep to myself (though Stefan has tolerated it, with a slightly pained look).

Avakum, our youngest, lost a soldier brother last week. I drove him to his village for the family funeral. His silence in the car was like a shroud. Then he started to talk. Why can't God help us? Where is he? He began crying and covered his eyes. He sat like that until we got closer to Babine and I had to ask directions, which made him sit up and take hold again. So I know that others have doubts too. We're simply not keen on admitting them.

I remember my own Spaso from the schoolyard on Symington Ave. He was the one who first made me see the world as it is. He called me a fairy and threw me against a fence and split open my head. I learned that a person can die at any time, that the life can just spill out of us — also that evil is human. There was another evil boy too, an Anglican church camp Spaso. There were jokes played at camp, humiliating kid stuff with shit and toilet paper. Spaso revelled in this stuff. He also caught toads and burned them with a magnifying glass. Mostly he just lay around on his bunk all day in a food-stained T-shirt. He was older, with pubic hair and an animal smell I found exciting even though I knew he was loathsome.

I've thought, watching films, that people who exit the theatre at the first bloodshed might be our real saviours. Our saints. But we don't know how to venerate them. We think, Pity they can't take it. Maybe they're running from what might seduce them, might wear down the aversion. We can get a taste for almost anything.

xo Chris

AUGUST 5, 1994

Dear Chris,

Spaso is indeed a piece of work. Re changing tastes: if you've developed a taste for *djuveč* there's little hope for you. I'm glad Slobo's story has seduced you, if that's the word. I find myself terribly moved and torn by it — all that Yugo baggage I've shoved to the back of my ancestral closet.

I won't attempt a birthday call to a vestibule on a Serbian hill-top. Congratulations on your vigorous entry into mid-life. Forty remains a greater challenge for girls — not quite two years off for me.

I'll be on sabbatical by year's end, my first ever — eight months. I'll spend my days taping oral histories and poring over documents that mean nothing to 99.99% of the world's people, but to me reveal all of history in a nutshell. Meanwhile Kušić's text will goad me along. The work itself is a pleasure. Also somewhat more current than translating dusty old nationalist poetry (the curse of my graduate thesis). But there's a connection to the old rhetoric and Slobo understands it.

Mater called last week with news that she has congestive heart disease, so her plan now is to die after a dramatic family reunion. I promised I would be in Trieste for X-mas. Footloose thereafter, I'll head to Podgorica and settle into the archives. Will also take some holiday time in Kotor with Leo. You haven't met Leo. He's a sort of ex. It means you and I can connect in Kotor in January. Leo travels. The house is on a rock ledge overlooking the bay. Stunning view. I could book you in for a week when he's not there, which would be better for both of you. He will think you a rival, and if he thinks you're gay there will be a different tension.

I was thinking of our history, yours and mine. Dubrovnik '91, routed by the Serboslav Navy. Nikšić and Ostrog your first summer. Then Mt. Durmitor and the Podgorica car project. We became friends in those weeks. Nikšić again last summer. You were worried about eviction from the fold — and coy about eros in the cloisters. I didn't press, and haven't since. This June: the Chetnik bar boys, the enigmatic choirmaster, and your hunger for more of Slobo's circles of hell and faint hope. We each have our understanding of the world and the Yugo catastrophe. We thrive on the challenge, the parry and thrust of thoughts without fear of judgement. I am a little bossy sometimes. You quickly counter it or become remote if I press too far. We have a rapport.

So, after weeks of indecision, I'll now tell you that I found the note in your car from "S" saying he had to break away from you, that you were drawing him from God, that the butcher's boy was a "knife to his heart" and so on. (The *butcher's boy?* Is this code or the real thing?) I didn't snoop. On our second jaunt to Priječko you stopped to get coffee. I looked in the glove box for some matches. Instead I found your lover's words, so beautifully scripted. It took me seconds to read them; I saw you returning, I closed it all away. Is it wise to leave this in your car? Perhaps you'd forgotten it was there. You will correct me if I'm wrong but it took just a moment's thought before the choirmaster came to mind. In the dining room I noticed a tension between you, also the way he assessed me with his eyes, like I was some sort of tart or harpy. He is certainly the pick of the bunch by any measure (I wouldn't know every measure). I'm aware that this affair might have begun almost two years ago. It's quite understandable that you'd keep it under wraps, but I feel I shouldn't conceal what I know. It must be a great strain now for both of you. His note suggests that he fell hard, and of course I wonder how all of this has affected you. Was (is) it love? You probably think I don't consider such things. But they do present themselves. I nearly deleted this paragraph.

I note that Bosnian Serbs have rejected the latest half-baked peace plan, while Milošević calls them war profiteers and says he will cut off their supplies from Belgrade: Daddy Slobo chiding naughty Karadžić just to give him a sloppy kiss later on. Meanwhile, Slobo calls General Mladić in from Goražde for a strategic tête-à-tête. Ratko Mladić shows every sign of being a four-star Spaso. Will anyone save us from this madness?

xx

Toni

AUG 28, 1994

Dear Toni,

I was terribly annoyed at myself for leaving Stefan's letter there. It's in front of me now, along with yours. I've had two days to consider your words, your subtexts and how I should reply, and now I see there is no reason for me to be embarrassed or angry or anything but relieved — that I can share it with you. I've told no one about Stefan and me, not even Axel.

It was Stefan himself who put the letter in the glove box. It had been slipped under my door when I was out. I found it just after dinner and went to his room. We talked and our voices started to rise. We went out to my car and drove down to the main road where I parked in a turnaround by the river. Coming down he was talking about betrayal, how his heart was hardened. I stayed silent. This was April. The day was freakishly mild. We had to roll down our windows to release the heat. The river was a torrent with chunks of ice in it and the sound filled the car. I still had the letter in my pocket. I took it out and referred to various florid phrases. I said it was all so unnecessary, that he'd turned our few brief encounters into a complex relationship, when really it was just about simple affection and lust. Feeling guilty about the butcher boy (you saw him the morning you left, the one-armed hunk, getting into his truck), I went on the attack and said all the wrong things, said he had spoiled a fine thing. I ploughed on through, squelching his interruptions, and then I folded the letter, put it back in the envelope and held it out to him, like an eviction notice. Turning the tables. And that's exactly what I didn't want. I wanted things not to change. But emotion ruled. He gazed at me with exquisite martyrdom, said something about straying from the path, knowing his way back. He held the letter in his fingers, his eyes shining. I was stone. He closed it ceremoniously into the glove box, stared at the river for a moment, got out of the car. He stood bent toward me with a hand on the open door. I remember this so clearly: the sun was on his face, the very last rays of sun from the horizon. He stood there glowing. He said I was free now. I could go to my Chetnik lover. I was speechless. If anyone was at all close to a lover, in potential at least, it was Stefan. But that was impossible, as this whole mess was proving. He clicked the door closed without any force, as if he had no anger. It was perfect, a command performance. I stayed in the car and for a long time I just stared at the river, at ice jamming up, slipping into the torrent again. I felt tears coming and I fought them. We're both adults. We made choices. I forced nothing on him. I certainly wasn't going to drive back to Strastanica to pass him climbing the stony track like some mythic penitent. I drove to Priječko and went into Čeko's and ordered beer, moved on to brandy, watched the RTS news, then some unidentifiable war film — blood and explosions. There were some boys at the bar cheering whenever anyone got shot. This is utterly typical of a late night at Čeko's but instead of diverting me, it just made me more miserable.

Our first encounter happened more than a year ago. We had a sort of friendship developing, though quite formal. His love of music is intense, so we connected on that. And he's a city boy, was a student for years in Belgrade, so he likely had some sort of gay life — which he will not discuss. Sex with men not only breaks his vows but in itself commits an abominable sin. He is very tender in bed. We managed to meet in the guest quarters (access screened by a grove of hawthorn, if you recall) perhaps five or six times, spread over about a year, and that was the full extent of the sex. I don't know how Stefan arranged entry. I do know that Petko, as our resident handiman, has keys to rooms. Petko is not a monk, in fact seems quite unpious, skipping prayers and spending hours in his room listening to the radio. He's young and has a sort of shaggy-dog appeal. It is my feeling (no direct proof) that Petko is an erotic pressure valve for some of the brethren. So hawthorn screens may not be needed; some things are obscured by simple discretion (there's that handy vow of silence again). I imagine none of this surprises you. I've told Axel the basics of some of it, but nothing about Stefan because (I'm just working this out) it felt so illicit right from the beginning, as if hinting anything to anyone would have been a heartless and damaging betrayal, and also an admission that I'd become a sort of wolf (or peacock) in the henhouse, cat among pigeons, devil's emmisary ... But it was Stefan who came to my room one morning and told me he wanted me. He needed a voice to round out the choir. He'd spoken with Abbot, it was all arranged. Then he kissed me in the brotherly way and I felt the lust in him.

It wasn't till months later, in a spring fever I suppose, that I touched him. The endless unconsummation finally wore me down. We'd gone to look for mushrooms in the woods above the pond. I went out after breakfast with Stefan and Gerasim. It was a lovely sunny morning. There were no mushrooms. After a while

Gerasim said he was going back. Stefan led me further on. From the moment Gerasim left us the outing became something else. Without speaking we climbed along the stream course until we reached an old ruin, broken stone walls beside a pool at the base of some rapids. We stood on a ledge of rock between the sun-warmed wall and the bubbling water. I reached out and touched his back, and he closed his eyes and tilted his head, and looked a model of Christian forbearance as I moved my fingers in little circles against the cloth of his robe. Then we began to play. And after that came the guest house encounters, widely separated. I don't think we ever matched the first thrill.

But Čeko's. When I left the bar it was raining hard and I was drunk. I drove home with elaborate care. Not far from Strastanica the headlights illumined Stefan on his knees in the mud, face lifted heavenward. Of course he'd had no plan to budge from this tableau as long as I was due to pass, and of course I stopped and told him to be sensible and get in the car. The rain was lashed by a cold wind and I was suddenly twitchy with anger at his stupidity. I got out of the car and hauled him to his feet. He stared into my face like a drowned Jesus. I dragged him round and opened the passenger door. He wept, sobbing, all the way back, and told me to stop at the foot of the drive so he could calm himself. It was all so overwrought and unprecedented. As we sat there with the heater blasting and the windows fogged over, the rain drumming on the roof, Stefan attempting to strangle back each wracking sob as it emerged, I felt like I'd been torn from my own life and dropped into someone else's. I took his hand and held it in both of mine, and I said I was sorry. Just said it quietly a few times and held his hand, watching my own hands in the shadows carressing it. Then I was crying. But not just out of guilt or regret. It was directly for his sorrow. I'd never seen anything like it — it was like spiritual convulsions. Maybe he was crying for all the other things too. I'd been the catalyst for a larger release. His sister and a cousin were killed in the first weeks of the war. He's never spoken more than a few terse words about it. He seemed always so strong and reasoned in his faith and his knowledge and acceptance of pain, and he still seems that way to me. In the car that day it all disintegrated. I thought, This is a crisis of faith. This is a turning point for him. His hand gave no response to me. But I couldn't let go. I just waited and held on, and his sobbing gradually subsided.

That awful night was four months ago. For a while afterward we spoke only about necessary musical things, but too pointed a chill between us only serves to make our divorce more evident. I'm still inclined to feel responsible. But the fire was in him too. There was a secret in the air around us for months before anything came of it. Even in the thick of the affair (spread pretty thin, admittedly) we didn't talk much. The sex was about basking in the secret pleasure, lying next to each other in that tawdry room, caressing, saying those excrutiating things people say like, I love the jut of your brow, or, What is that little scar there? It was I who said those things. Stefan, with a hint of a contented smile, answered concisely or stayed silent. It was such a wonderful thing to see him and know him like that those few times, uncloistered. But I think I was engaged in a sort of play-acting of falling in love again, with no weight to it. Because I'm still with Pimm. It's been four years now and I still feel him there, he's still a discerning voice in me and a standard by which I measure myself and others. So with Stefan I was playing, but he was in earnest. I probably knew that but blinded myself to it. Our encounters were made more intense by the restriction — they were fraught with Romance. His sudden crisis woke me up to the fact. His misery, of course, was real. And his Romance was, to my mind, a longing for escape and life in the world — and all such earthly desire is a monk's failure. Our secret knowledge is still there, in limbo. But I think I was wrong about Stefan having a major spiritual crisis. Keeping the faith is largely about skillful evasion. You simply don't allow certain items to enter the agenda.

I'm a part of this place — its rituals and its subterfuge. Certainly my donation encourages Nikolaj to please me. But he has allowed me to be more a participant than a guest, while the question of my spiritual life remains unresolved. Sometimes I think Nikolaj knows everything. He has that look in his eye. He's a generous man behind his crusty facade, and a forgiving one, I hope.

I'm glad you found Stefan's note, even gladder that you said so.

xo

Chris

AUG 30/94

Dear Axel:

For your info I include copies of two letters. I'm sorry for the quality of Toni's but Nikolaj's photocopier seems to be early Soviet. Now you have before you the full report on Stefan from

119

two vantage points. Re Jovan: he just delivers to the kitchen now. The thrill is gone. I also began to resent his dislike for washing.

Your birthday greeting and the picture of you and doggie are propped on my desk. Please kiss Oscar for me. You will soon (finally) have some photos of me in situ: I'm muddy, digging onions. Toni took the pics. You'll see me beardy and thinner, lean from two years of hiking. Sorry to not send sooner, but you know I've never been a camera bug, nor are the brothers. You look very urban-arty on your new sofa with Oscar and his smart haircut. No Art Shoppe sofas here, and certainly no mini-schnauzers, coiffed or otherwise. And no birthday party unless you're a saint. Turning forty has felt like a non-event.

What I remember lately, very fondly, are those long boozy multi-course dinners we used to have on Dundonald or at your place with you and Rick, or just with you. Do you stay in touch with Rick?

That's all — would be unconscionable to stuff this envelope any thicker. Do you see Toshi still? Perhaps you'll let me know if he's changed addresses and I'll send him a note. I thought this morning that I'd neglected him since Bernard's death — since Pimm's actually. We had such good times with them.

xoxo Chris

SEPTEMBER 23, 1994

Dear Chris,

Stefan in the rainstorm was some sort of ghastly pinnacle of Jesus hysteria pathos — very glad I didn't experience it for real. Your letter was full of revelations. Thank you.

I should have more Slobo text for you, with luck, in late October. I've got some here too that I've barely glanced at, and Martin says the next instalment is on the way. Can't keep up. But I can give it full focus in Kotor. If you join me there in the New Year you'll get the latest.

xo
Antonia

SEPT 25

Dear Chris,

I phoned twice on Saturday but couldn't get through. Regarding Stefan, I'm not speechless exactly, but I remind you that more than once you denied, *point blank*, that you were fucking the brothers. You fed me Jovan — a little fantasy thrill that threw me very effectively off the scent. I can see that Toni has become a close friend. I called her this weekend to thank her for invading your glove box. Why the big secret? You say it was only play, or "play-acting" — but you protest too much about it meaning nothing. If Pimm is the ideal then love still remains the ideal. If it can happen again he would want that. I'm not sure why I'm encouraging this because I don't want you to get hurt, OR to stay there forever.

Stefan's breakdown in the rain was desperately sad. It was spiritual, yes, but hardly just religious. It's complicated, as you said — sin, the war, we don't know what else. But in the car, all I could see was you loving him.

I won't say more. Except that the culture clash, and all that God stuff, must be a challenge for both of you. Don't spare me any more details. I want to know everything.

Toshi is back on West 4th, same address, he evicted his sublet. Bernard left him the condo and he sold, so he's got some savings. He just had a piece in *Vanity Fair*. Physically, at least, he's healthy.

Looking at your letter (the short one to me, as opposed to your epistle to Toni), it seems like you're homesick enough to come visit. Why not come for my birthday? Make it two weeks and we can hop to NY and see Toni, Toshi, Derek & Kent, and we'll go out for some culture, and subculture, if you remember how. I'm going to make a phone call. I just called my travel people. Phone Atlas in Dubrovnik, 442-357. You fly Dubro to Zagreb, Munich, Toronto. Or fly Munich to NY and I'll meet you there, but you have to spend some time here too. All this print and phone chat is not enough. I walked by the house last week and I thought of Max in his cigar box under those cheesy orange marigolds. But we won't go past the house. Only if you want to.

Much Love,

Axel

Chapter Nineteen

I couldn't deny Axel the visit. I informed Nikolaj, expressing my regret, telling him I had family matters to tie up in Toronto. The same day, after chant practice, I told Stefan and he began to smoulder. He cast it as concern for the choir: I'd be gone almost three weeks over November and December, jeopardizing our readiness for the Christmas concert in January. He'd been planning a short choral work of his own, his first ever. Without my voice in rehearsals he'd be unable to properly polish the piece. And the concert, as always, was important for bringing in donations and luring new parishioners. These things were said with stifled emotion in front of the brothers as we broke up from rehearsal. With almost three months to rehearse before Christmas my absence seemed to me insignificant, and as Stefan became more insistent I said so. The brothers wandered off to leave us to it, their faces masked with indifference. The twins prepared to extinguish the candles Stefan insisted on burning through rehearsals despite Nikolaj's chafing at the cost. (I loved Stefan's ability to win minor contests with the boss. No one else could do it.)

Stefan told the boys to leave the candles lit and to join the others for supper, we'd follow in a moment. We were left standing in the warm glow. Stefan went and pulled the side door shut in his measured, focused way. He stood with his back to me, head bowed.

"Stefan, let's go and eat. Before they miss us."

He minutely shook his head.

"Stefan?"

"We have come to limit."

"What?"

"Limit. Crossing point."

"Really. Well a crossing is not a limit."

"I don't want English lesson."

"I didn't mean that."

"You want to speak Serbian now?"

"No. Don't be witchy."

"Okay, you must face truth. Why you are here."

"That's such a complex question."

"Ah. Run in circle, you see?"

"I'm devoted to this place — you know that."

"Why do you run away?"

"I'm not running. I have obligations. I haven't left here for two years. A few trips to see Toni."

"She is nothing. No consequence."

"To you, yes, obviously. I want to see my friends. A few weeks."

"I see, come and go, please yourself, live in Strastanica Hotel."

"That's not fair and simply not true!"

"Do not shout."

"I love it here. I love the separation from the world."

He stared incredulously at me.

"From the world? What world? Strastanica is in world. Listen to artillery!"

"Of course, but —"

"What do you want? Just singing? Live with nature?"

"It's much more. You know I have moments. Moments of transcendence."

"What do you see?"

"I don't know what to call it."

"You must call it God. Problem is, you search but not believe. Never make your committal. Do you know, you are one lucky man. Other monastery, other abbot, you will be pushed out of the doors. Gone. *Zbogom!*"

"Yes, yes, probably."

"*Ne.* Not probable. This is sure. Any other abbot from here, any monastery, you name, Sopočani, Studenica, Žiča, not easy way for you. Nikolaj is big gift to you. Not only because you give also to us. Do you understand?"

"He's not doctrinaire."

"*Šta?*"

"He bends the rules. I know. I'm grateful. But I can't just break my relationships with others, leave everything behind. Axel is my dearest friend."

"I thought he was brother."

"No. A friend."

"You said brother."

"Yes."

"Why do you lie?"

"Well, obviously, when I first came here, I couldn't risk having you know I was gay."

Our eyes held on each other. I had an crazy impulse to laugh. Stefan moved away.

"Then he is lover."

"No. Never a lover. He's my friend. If he were my lover, would I be here for two years without him? Axel needs Toronto, New York, he's a city boy and always will be. But when I think of the village in Toronto —"

"Village?"

"The gay village, the neighbourhood."

"Ah, such folly."

"Someday we'll debate that. But anyway I don't want to be there. The noise, the social whirl, the life I had ... it's all past. All gone. Strastanica feels more like home now."

"But Chris, you are confessed pagan."

"I have my own beliefs."

"Impossible. You pretend you know everything."

"That's exactly what you do!"

He angled his head back, stared at me like I was an unfathomable idiot.

"Who keeps secret of Chris from Nikolaj? You are such heep, heep ..."

"Hypocrite?"

"Yes! I'm hiding for you so Nikolaj does not know how much you reject God. And still you sing for God. From your heart. But you have stupid idea — stupid! — that you are only flesh."

"Not only."

"Okay. Flesh and confusion. Flesh and warm feeling that means nothing. Nice feeling for other people. People floating on feelings, like lifeboat, ready to sink."

"We're all ready to sink. So are you."

"Yes. Ready. But I am rising and you sink more deep. Faith makes you rise."

"You indulge in hypocrisy of the flesh too."

"I confess mine. I pray for help. That is difference."

"This is a pointless discussion."

"No, I'm enjoying. You are boring now?"

"Of course not."

"Question of God is never pointless."

"It just can't be answered."

"Ah, Chris, Chris ... You fear this answer."

Stefan moved off to the big icon of Sava. He stared up at the saint's bearded, drooping face.

"You are like Miloš who came to us from Valjevo. 1989. He was novice for one year, made beautiful objects of wood. The semantron that calls us to prayer, this he made. Then he goes to Valjevo for visit and sends postcard: I can't come back. I have good job in factory. He makes furniture. Okay. Then he joins militia and sends picture with gun, smiling."

"How on earth is that like me, Stefan?"

"You do not have gun. But same thing. You have sinking, fear of death or of suffering, anger for it, for no meaning, anger for loss. And fear too of black things inside you, of your weakness. When gun is used is always from these things. But when the man stays with God, only with his God and in life of faith, there is no gun and no sinking. And no death."

"I don't believe that. We die. We die from old age or sickness or war or whatever, no telling what. But we die."

"Chris, you make me very sad. Very sad."

"Okay. You want my voice, you want my constant commitment, total devotion, the rejection of my friends and my past ...

You want too much. You can't have every piece of me. It's not yours to have and I won't give it."

"Not having. I don't want. It's giving. Not to me. Give to God. Open your heart."

"Oh, please. I'm sorry, I'm very sorry, but there are questions that need answering before I can swallow God's perfect love."

"Maybe you need bigger test. Not questions from your mind. Hardest questions come from the suffering, the suffering that mind can't understand."

"Stefan, the bigger the test and the worse the suffering, the less I believe. I've been tested. And I won't talk about it because words don't equal it, they don't come close. I lost someone, who I loved."

I'd said it. I couldn't go on. Something rose inside me. My throat closed up. My eyes burned and my head began to swim. I fought it hard. It came anyway and overwhelmed me. I sank to the steps under the iconostasis, tears and mucus flowing, shaming me with my nakedness. Stefan disappeared behind the doors of the altar. Then he was beside me again with a towel. He sat next to me on the steps and I wiped my hands and face. I regained control. I stared at the crumpled towel in my hands. Stefan had given me a clean Eucharist linen. I looked across the clear expanse of the sanctuary to the pocked and stained saints, and they seemed to glower at me from the shadows. Stefan touched my cheek and I let the gentle pressure turn my face to his. He had a faint smile.

"It was not consecrated."

He meant the towel. Then he was looking into me. He looked into me with a calm searching that was ... Well, no one had ever done it. Not even Pimm. I couldn't take it. I broke the gaze.

"Stand up," he said.

We stood, and he began a prayer. The simple melody infused the air around us with its knowledge of beauty and sorrow, with what the monks call joyful mourning. But as Stefan sang I wasn't feeling the presence and pull of hidden mysteries, not the way I might during the liturgy or in the forest or while working in the garden. What I felt was him. Stefan's spirit was calming me, and filling me up.

Chapter Twenty

OCTOBER 1941

Vedrana's tears would not stop. She stood in a dry autumn breeze on the sloping ground below the Žepa feedmill and gazed at a clodded mound of earth. Sun glanced from the wet that slicked her cheeks, proving her weakness and spurring my own show of bravery. It was nothing for a drunken soldier to waste a few bullets on a scavenging old dog. Surely Vedrana knew this, as we all did. Even Aunt had dabbed her eyes only briefly, pricked by her niece's sorrow and her own memories of puppyish Garo, then she had turned again to necessity, the questions of what we would eat today, how to ease the swelling of her boy's ulcered hand, why Uncle was still coughing under his blanket at noon and would not stir himself to search for firewood.

Scrounging dogs inflame war's pinched resentments; dead, they ease them. Others in the Žepa feedmill would balk as we gave Garo his scraps. "The mutt is half-dead already — look at his ribs!" One less hungry dog is a mercy all round. "Bury him!" said the woman in her doorway. She stood there often, frowning on the feedmill comings and goings, holding a ruddy infant. She called to cousin Željko and me as we stood over Garo, stunned by the glistening crimson pool in the dry mud of the street. We'd heard the two shots. Then a boy came to tell us what had passed and led us to the body. "You boys! If that's your animal, take him away and bury him!"

We each grasped Garo by a hind leg and dragged him to the mill. We didn't cry. We searched about and found an old shovel and dug a shallow hole in the weedy earth as Vedrana sobbed. She knelt and smoothed the matted fur, recoiled and stood and gave in to a flood of tears and mucus. Uncle was informed but remained under his blanket. He too had said that we fed Garo too much. Later he came to the grave and stared in his inept inspector's way, saying finally that we must pile some rocks to keep the vermin away. He hacked and spat and scanned for rocks, then pointed helpfully to a gully running down from the road. "Old Garo," he said, nodding. "It was God's will." He went back up the slope to smoke and shrug with the old men. We fetched and piled our rocks, soothed by repetition and the visible result.

Aunt's voice rolled down the hill. She was berating Uncle before the assembly of ancients, grief and rage fuelling a spectacular aria. She flayed him with her voice. Uncle flung a few words, but they were like mouse squeaks to a roaring lion. He went off in search of firewood.

The feedmill held eight families in three large rooms. For one night there was a ninth, but they were squeezed out by morning. Our eight became the acknowledged limit beyond which civility was impossible. By tacit agreement we were all 100% Serb. Our family became hyper-Serbs, partly out of collective need, partly in fear that our impurity might be discovered.

When there was flour, women would bake a *kolač* for their Saint's Day, and sing prayers with the family. On Sundays we would all pray together, asking God to protect and save us. Aunt told us to pray that the Ustashas be driven from Višegrad. I asked her why God let the Ustashas live to do such evil. She spoke some platitudes, but I persisted until she snapped at me: "Never mind! God does what he pleases!" Then she crossed herself and bustled to her duties.

In the mill we made little households, which we secluded by hung blankets or rags stitched together. Our water came from the mill stream. Our latrine was a slope-roofed shed covering two storage tanks with heavy iron covers. These tanks generated a story. When the first families had arrived that July, the children had been the first ones to peer into the dark holes in the shed. Two boys had squatted and together loosed their bowels into the inviting unknown. Next morning a grandpa lowered a little bucket on a string into each hole and discovered kernels of barley in one tank and corn in the other. The bucket was employed and grain hauled up, accompanied by mingled mirth and horror among the children. The women set to, pounding or soaking the grain, making bread and porridge that the children either refused to eat or first picked through with cringing attention. Soon enough a thoroughly tainted bucket was raised, and a righteous child tattled. The grain remained too precious to be rendered useless by a few familiar turds, but in any case it was depleted within a month or two, and so the storage tanks then became officially what the boys had already christened them. The source became the terminus, and none too soon, for the privy attached to the mill had long since been overflowing.

The women cooked together outdoors on a square of pavement. It was said the year had been good for crops, but the people of Žepa did not part easily with their store against war and winter. We grew thin. Aunt's cushion of fat melted away and her face became sharp. Meat existed only in memory. One day two men and a woman appeared in a Red Cross truck and gave us tinned beef, hard salted fish, some oil, flour, sugar and medicines, then they left with most of their load still intact. I saw them stop also at the mosque before they drove on into the mountains. The food was contentious. What to carefully divide? What to pool for the communal cooking? The women disputed. As cooking began each child gnawed a portion of fish, so salty it burned our lips.

When not charged with gathering wood or water, washing pots or performing any number of unskilled but essential tasks, we children made our own entertainment. With my cousins and other boys I followed the stream down to where we would cross it on a thick rotting log and roam in scrubby woodland. There we would become warriors. The far side of the stream was dubbed Croatia, the near side our own Bosnia, or sometimes Serbia. We would divide up and shoot each other from behind tree trunks with stick rifles. Croats and Serbs, Serbs and Muslims, Serbs and Germans and Italians, every combination indiscriminate, switching allegiance on a whim as we rose from death and our battles were renewed. Croats were the most villainous. As Croats we took special pleasure in dying horribly, screaming and flailing, flinging ourselves to earth and posing in grotesque heaps. I would sometimes be a Muslim commander, thinking obliquely of my secret

Turkish blood. My Islamic army was made to begin each battle with prostrations to the East, just as our Serbs and Croats would cross themselves and call on Christ. There were arguments over whether Croats knew Christ, over how and even *if* they crossed themselves. My father had told me long ago that Croats could be recognized by their backward signing of the cross. With the other boys I could be arrogant and assured on this point and so they acquiesced.

In a copse of small trees and scrubby underbrush by the stream there was an enclosed place, a sort of cavern with walls formed of tangled branches and greenery. This was our prisoner of war camp. Here prisoners were tied to trees and to each other. Sometimes we were forced to use imaginary rope, which was often more gratifying, for all escapees were shot dead. From our conjoined unconscious we found devilish inspiration, inventing crude punishments and humiliations. Boys were obliged to strip and perform vile acts. Organs and orifices were made proximate in games of violation and presumed disgust. One boy, runty and inept, was moved to real humiliation and real tears — the worst of failures. He was marched out of the woods and sent back to mama, his silence bought with a threat that I myself uttered. The moment shames me. I said I would cut off his little thing and turn him into a girl. Then I rejoined my comrades to further our descent. But we knew how to balance savagery with pleasure: when the one became indistinguishable from the other, when both attack and submission furnished equal but divergent delights, our games were at their most sublime. Thus we began to imagine that horrors were natural and inevitable, and not without their rewards.

So when later my German lieutenant confined me and forced his seduction, I recognized both him and myself, and saw a convergence of truth borne upon our shared misery.

Gentle reader! Knowing of such prisons, you may well ask how we might escape them! How do we become free of our inadequate blundering selves? In 1989 I came to know a priest in Medvedja. Zlata and Rajko took me to services and parish dinners at the church there, and finally to the Christmas Day service. This priest struck me with his manner. He had no arrogance, only a gentle certitude. He had no insistence, only calm authority. He seemed to live in a near constant state of revelation, of being wonderstruck, which, being so constant, gave him no look of dumb joy but simply an aura of rapt engagement, a harmony with each present and imminent moment. In conversation, his face was both open and opening to the world, his eyes deep and glimmering, asking one to enter, to partake. His cheeks above his greying beard were scarred, his nose a little crooked, yet this face radiated beauty. When he sang the liturgy, his strong voice (though unschooled, a bit shaky in pitch) filled the church like warm light. When on Sundays and Saint's Days I kissed his hand and, like a hundred before and after me, accepted from it the bread said to be God, he would look into my face and say "The Body of Christ" with such utter lack of reservation, such clear and celebratory *knowledge*, that I found myself stricken with love.

I could also believe that this man concealed shrewdness and enjoyed his power. He may have run rampant as a youth, may have "raised hell," and now he wished to avoid a personal descent. There are multiple questions: Is the priest privy to Truth? If not, what is his own singular truth? (For we all have ideas of heaven and earth, good and evil, which we cherish and will not reveal, and each our own stratagems, ways of parcelling and storing away the world's terrors.) Is the priest simply a man of good works and social graces who has found peace? How far might his peace extend?

With shining countenance and stirring voice the priest preached to the people on Christmas morning 1990, and his words were these: "Christ is born! If He is pure in our hearts we are assured of eternal life." And something else: "Only with full and unwavering faith in Orthodoxy, which is the true word of God, can we triumph over false gods and the spread of Islam."

In our boys' war camp captured Muslims were made to kiss a cross of sticks. As our repertoire of humiliations increased, we learned more about our fellows. The boy of six or seven who we had banished and sent sniffling to his mother had the rare and freakish misfortune to be circumcized. Bound hand and foot, his pants at his ankles, he was made to kiss the true Serbian pizzles of true warrior Serbs, each little knob shielded with its God-given foreskin. The sons of Saint Prince Lazar laughed at the infidel's tiny naked thing. "*Balija!*" they shouted — an ancient word, the worst name one can fling at a Muslim. I joined them, bravely presenting my wrinkled foreskin on its stubby pole, thanking my Serb father that he had kept a mullah's knife from it. And I spewed oaths like the Chetniks who had appeared in the hills that very spring, killing *balije* for sport on the back roads, among them my own mother and her friend on their way to Sjeciŝta market.

What confusion we dwell in. I might easily have been the circumcized, the whimpering boy in our POW camp, or a taunting

Muslim boy in the woods behind Žepa's mosque. It can become so very clear, if one allows the unbidden flash of empathy to become insight, that none of us is a chosen people, though surely some peoples are damned. We insist on distinction, creating only a collective blur of tears and wretchedness. By chance, not being among the wretched or the murdered, we are inspired by the spectacle or the corpse. So when two bloating corpses were discovered in a swampy part of our woods, a boy had to poke with a stick at their blackened privates and swollen bellies, while others were content to watch his performance, transfixed. A few had the decency to be sick after they'd come to their senses. Days and weeks later, mothers awoke to screams and shook their thrashing sons awake to say they were safe, all was well, the rotting man was only a dream. Certainly we were all plagued in the night by fantastical torments. But I had kinder dreams too, dreams of joining the brave fighters and becoming a hero like my absent Partisan father.

The Partisans! Brothers and sisters and lovers fighting arm in arm! Serbs and Croats, Montenegrins and Muslims and Slovenes, a few Jews and even Gypsies — all joined in prickly harmony. Women drove tanks and became officers. They gave orders to the men! A vast commune of South Slavs one day would stretch from Trieste to Skopje and beyond. Father was never a man who trusted exclusive gods. To revive a heart sickened by clannish tyranny, he cast his lot with Tito's unifying dream. Carrying arms for the great Marshal, he was recharged with purpose. War can indeed make peace. We must only choose the side of honour, grit our teeth and pass through the maelstrom.

Stooped in my little attic at Mali Voćnjak, I stared at an old schoolbook and was crowded by memory, by "Yugo-nostalgia," as the nationalists shrewdly say. In this ink-smudged text of pseudo history printed on thin postwar paper I saw the teenage scrawl of my own name, the stains of greasy fingers, the stamp inside the dog-eared cardboard cover: *Priboj Middle School*, and I recalled my teacher Mr. Suljić. He had let us keep the old texts when the pristine new edition was distributed. In the still heat of my attic I turned the flimsy yellowed pages. Tito's dearly bought victory over the Fascist-bourgeois chimera was painted in prose that glowed on the page like burnished gunmetal. One could almost scent the cordite! Here were grainy photos of strewn bodies and dead horses, wrecked trucks and tanks, men face down in the snow with dark stains spreading. Here was Tito in his felt cap with the Communist star, his face set in creases of resolve. Here he was again on a rubble-strewn street with a bevy of officers and a mangy pack of captured Italians. Here were columns of tattered soldiers and packhorses trudging up a switchback trail on the naked flank of a mountain. "Four thousand comrades died that November," said the text.

In his doomed Bosnian house stood a wet-eyed balding coot, school memories and heroic sacrifice rising round him like ghosts. Tito had triumphed, smashed his enemies on all fronts: Hitler and Mussolini, Chetnik Royalists and puppet Croat Fascists. And Yugoslavia had peace. A peace of exhaustion. For more than forty years a peace merely of enmity stifled, cowed by the coercions of a new religion and its pantheon of three: Brotherhood, Unity, and Josip Broz Tito. Now that temple too is fallen, even the rubble bulldozed into the mud, and we have come full circle back to the boys in the woods: running in packs, destroying the Other and dishonouring his body, marking our gain of wasted land.

Enough. We must attempt a strategy of good cheer. Or at least of dogged hope. Raise a glass of *vinjak*. Another. A toast to all true South Slavs. To Croats! To Serbs! To Franjo and Slobo! Never mind the silly disputes, the unfortunate deaths, the burned villages, the paltry loss of Vukovar and its smug Austrian facades. Dubrovnik needed to be knocked down a peg or two as well, with its tourist pandering and haughty Mediterranean airs. Indeed all Croats, if they face up, will concede they've enjoyed the fat of the land for too long. (We can easily ignore the Slovenes. Let them go on licking the nether parts of Austria.) So let us even the field and share our great Balkan legacy. Together, though duly apart, we will rekindle the patriot fires and save ourselves from the hectoring West and its self-serving conspiracies. To Arkan! Arkan our warrior prince and his fearsome Tigers who save us from the breeding Turks. O we are tired of these Turks! Forced to smile at them across fences and over bank and shop counters! Always trying to keep our children from casually tainting the pedigree with Ottoman blood. It often seems hopeless. This dream of cleansing our blood, our land, of making ourselves pure and whole and without defect. An impossible task. We have been lulled by proximity and neighbourly conduct, by wedding parties and house-raisings, borrowed horsecarts. We see that the longed-for purity will fail. Why can we not simply let it rest? Tend our chickens and our geranium pots and visit each other for coffee and brandy, slander the absent in sly asides. Can we not loathe each other in a civilized manner, smile and smile and let the vile heart curdle happily? Isn't this the daily routine the world over?

But events overtake us. War is scented on the wind. Then the enemy draws near and we must choose: run or fight. Courage is said to be its own goodness. Courage is linked to potency, and indeed our most wilfully virile men have a phrase, their variant of a universal sentiment. Following a triumphal ravishing of the love object, the strutting buck will exclaim to his mates, "I shot her a bullet!" This phrase, a parroting of soldiers, was employed one morning outside the Žepa feedmill by a pimple-faced colt named Vojo. With his pals in the cookyard at breakfast Vojo pitched the words a touch too loudly, and thus endured blows from a wooden spoon and a mother's scathing harangue.

The nearest thing to a real man in the Žepa mill was my wheezing Uncle Vaso. We were a makeshift clan of mothers and children, sickies, grandpas and grannies. But there were a few Vojos, boys with whisps of dark hair sprouting on upper lips, and there were many more girls in that ripening phase somewhat beyond girl-hood yet not properly marriageable. Cana was such a girl. I was a callow boy of nine, but I could acknowledge Cana's bloom when spurred by the insinuations of the older boys, even if I didn't quite share their virile imaginings — not, that is, until one bless-edly warm October day. Aunt had sent me for kindling, which had to be gathered farther and farther afield.

I found myself in the woods beyond the stream, well beyond even our miniature war zone. I was dawdling, taking the oppor-tunity to explore and daydream, and as I hiked through a stand of oak and came over a little rise I saw an older boy on all fours, pumping among the fiddlehead ferns. His white buttocks clenched and opened at me, and as his head turned I recognized Vojo. Cana's face was gazing over his shoulder at the sky. She looked bored. Then she saw me and gave a little scream, a trivial scream.

Vojo leapt up and stood looking from her to me with his pink pistol bobbing, and then Cana began to laugh, lightly, ethereally.

He wrestled with his pants and swore at her: "Why do you laugh? You whore. Stop it!" His pistol shrank. He got his pants up and cinched his belt, sneered at me. "What do you want, runt?" I was speechless.

Cana sat back against a tree trunk, her chin poised on raised knees, dark skirt pulled down to hide all but her woollen-stockinged ankles. We were all silent for a moment, Cana's eyes assessing us before she spoke: "Go away, Vojo. Go back now. Slobo has come to help me look for wood." Vojo didn't move. She glared at him. "You stink! Go away!"

Vojo moved off, swearing, calling her a piece of trash and other such dirty or worthless things. He disappeared over the hill, his voice receding.

Cana gazed at me. "What do you want, Slobo?"

I swallowed: "Aunt sent me for kindling." Holding my eyes with her own, she raised her skirt just a little, and laughed. Like tinkling bells. Then she yanked her skirt back. There, naked to the world, was her Vienna strudel with its soft beard, and below it the dark crack of her buttocks. Bits of dry forest litter clung to her creamy skin.

"Come and look." I turned my head to where Vojo had disappeared. "He's gone. Come. He knocked me down. I need to be examined."

Hana would later benefit from my dexterity. It helped to make up for my dearth of bullets and the misfiring of my pistol. Certainly Hana and I never discussed the ways of these things, or why sometimes in our bed I became abruptly cold and far away and had to go to the kitchen for a calming brandy. She of course knew nothing of Cana's inspired instruction, or of my invading German lieutenant, or of the girls later at Priboj Middle School who shied from my inept courting or, accepting me, watched me succumb to a mortified inertia. Never predictable, Eros has for me often been unfathomable. The mind doctors might have me probe these matters. But I know enough.

My Hana. She was much her own Hana too. A now sweet, now formidable mystery. A judge, looking at me askance. A gentle healer, indulging me like a child. She had a moral force. When we fought she usually won. Then the fire went out of her. I avoid her ghost, which is my infernal immutable memory, the things I once had. After Marko's death I saw her lost by increments both to me and to herself, finally so surfeited with grief she was unable to leave her bed, converse, or show a glimmer of affection. She became shrunken, her face scored by pain. I loved her as nothing before or since. And the vaulting dome of that love, filled with light, shrank at last to a burnt cinder in a black night. My heart that had expanded so, had filled with wonder, my heart infused with heat and humming with the certainty of goodness, my heart as the months and years passed bathed in a settling warmth, a daily balm against the pricking world, this living heart became a cold inert stone, a thing that can feel nothing and shed no tears.

When grief finally rose inside me in Zlata's car on the swelter-ing road to Priština Hospital, I began what is called healing, but really it remains only an uneasy truce with the gods who robbed me. I'll not further bare the wound by writing of Marko. I confess I don't know how to write about Marko's death; the attempt floods me with bile and bitterness, and the lurking thought, desperately pushed back into the shadows, that I did not love him well enough. My solution (as you know) is to write of other deaths: those ones removed enough to inspire awe or anger or rapt abhorrence, but not grief. Grief and language do not intersect. What we can express is sadness or distress or some form of the tragic, but those who have known grief will not find it on a page.

I have delayed redemption too long. Let there be a glimmer. There remains hope of escape, of a new life. In 1945 was born a child of war and fleeting passion. My father died for Tito before he could know his second son. I encountered my half-brother for just a few hours one summer afternoon, before he vanished from our lives. It was said he escaped to more fertile soil. Where and who might he be now? A captain of industry in Belgium? A carpenter in London? A NATO officer moving his troops around an ungrateful foreign land? I have a simpler vision. He is a U.S. postal delivery man. What is his dream? To escape. From the endless round of picket fences and yards like golf greens and titanic cars floating serenely on oceans of pavement; from dogs whose long chains daily, comically, arrest their frenzied charge with a snap, the gleaming teeth a hair's breadth from the terrified mailman's ankle. Perhaps unknown Saša, renamed Davey or Doug, is on such a street now in Florida or Oklahoma. Or he could be dead of an acute instance of postal madness, a colleague with an illegal Kalashnikov and a grudge to settle — the American news that is most relished here. The news that the land of freedom and wealth is rotten underneath.

Chapter Twenty-one

I left the monastery early, giving myself a full day for the drive to Dubrovnik. Toni had arranged a dinner date for me with Martin Ivry and I hated the thought of bad roads or a November storm bringing me in late. It would be my first, maybe my only chance to talk directly to Martin about Slobo, also about the situation in Sarajevo. Stefan had cousins and friends there. Brother Maksim had close family. I'd brought some addresses with me on the chance that Martin could do a little digging and offer some news. Maybe he could even help them somehow, though he was likely swamped with such requests. I also wanted to know more about Slobo's past. It seemed conceivable there could be a link to Pimm: the half-brother, Saša.

When I'd climbed past Žabljak into Durmitor Park, I pulled into a roadside lookout and got out to stretch my legs. Cold gusts were whipping over the stone barrier fronting the carpark. The low wall gave onto a dizzying river gorge and beyond it forested hills, rising to stone peaks shadowed by cloud. The wind soon drove me back into the car. I knew this stretch of road. Two years before, Antonia and I had stopped to take in the view and she told me about the unique flora and fauna of the Durmitor preserve. She said the black pine was endangered. It was rare for her to express such affection for the land — in fact, for anything that might imply national pride.

The sky was now changing rapidly. The Golf shuddered in blasts of wind. I watched the mountains fade behind a wash lowering like a curtain. I knew these sky signs. The squall would most likely blow through and I'd be on my way again in sunshine.

A clump of birch clinging behind the wall heaved violently and released a spray of golden leaves that tumbled over the car. Sleet spattered the windshield, then turned to snow and thickened until I could barely see the wall in front of me. I turned on the wipers and watched them pack sodden snow at the margins. The light had an undersea density. As the rhythm of the sweeping blades lulled me I began to feel a gathering unreality — for everything: the place I was in, my past, the existence of Strastanica, of Stefan, of everyone, even of Pimm. Gone. Or just *non*, as if I had only imagined or dreamt all of it, dreamt the world. It felt like something was about to end or disappear, as if there was nothing else but this dim empty anticipation of a loss, or a ... nothingness. A chasm opening. There was no me. There was something, the world maybe, but not me in it. Then the wipers slapped. The snow was snow again. I felt the hot blast of the defroster on my face. The clock on the dash read half past eleven. There was a paper bag on the seat beside me: lunch. As long as it was storming, I might as well eat. Cold chicken, cheese, bread, and my own pickled peppers and spring onions, which I would have to fish from the jar with my fingers. Food made me real again.

The storm passed. Packing up my lunch things, I jumped as I heard a voice. A dripping face appeared at the window.

"*Dobar dan!*"

The man smiled, thrust a thumb over his shoulder, half turning toward the road. He hoisted a metal gas can and shouted through the glass. His car was stopped down the road, could I spare a few litres? He would pay in Deutschmarks. I looked at the gauge even as I recalled gassing up in Žabljak; the tank was full. I shut off the engine and got out.

"*Jeste! Nekoliko litara, nema problema.*"

He was young, twentysomething, in faded jeans and a red parka. No head cover. He was soaking wet. His ready Deutschmarks hinted that he was a black marketeer. I unlocked the Golf's tank and he thrust a clear plastic hose into the pipe, sucked briefly on the other end, then quickly lowered it into his battered gas can. As he straightened up the carpark was suddenly awash in sunlight, his face flash-lit against the dark horizon.

"Hey!" He looked skyward. "*Lijepo!*"

"*Da, blagoslov.*"

We concurred on the blessing of the sun. His eyes were blue above insomniac rings. His thick chestnut hair was dripping, plastered to his forehead. Attempting to offer him a towel, I instead heard the word for "gun" emerge from me. He stared at me in stupefaction before I quickly backpedalled.

"*Ne ne, izvinite.* Oh Christ. I mean for your hair — *osušiti kosa.* A towel."

"Ah. Word is *peškir.*"

"Yes. Thank you."

"Ne *puška. Puška* is gun."

"I know. Sorry."

"I am happy for towel. Thank you."

"Good."

"Not needing gun."

"Great."

I opened the trunk and got a towel from my bag. He briefly scrubbed his head with it.

"Better. Thank you."

He stared blankly out over the gorge.

"Snow is passing."

"Yes, thank God."

"Snow good only for ski."

"True."

"You ski?"

"A little. I mean I used to."

"America?"

"Canada. I'm Canadian, not American."

"Pardon."

"It's okay. Do you ski?"

"Never ski, no."

"So close to Durmitor!"

"Yes, close. But ..."

"But?"

"Not ski. Ski is for tourist."

"I see."

"You like skatting?"

"Skatting? Um ..."

"Ice, hockey skatting."

"Ah, well, not all Canadians like hockey."

"You don't like."

"Not really, no."

I recalled that my tank was being drained.

"Excuse me ... the gas?"

"Ah!"

He bent and peered into the can.

"You can fill up in Žabljak."

"I go to Podgorica. For business."

"There's a station in Žabljak. You can get back there on a litre or two."

"No time, my friend." He flashed a regretful smile.

"But while we talk, my friend, you're taking my gas."

"Is okay. I pay cash."

"That's fine but ... I'm sorry, what's your name?"

"Hariz."

"And I'm Chris."

"Please to meet."

"Hariz, I need my gas, not your money."

"Okay. No problem. But maybe is too late."

He peered into the can, yanked the hose from it. Gas spilled over the snow.

"I pay you extra."

"Very kind."

I eyed his jerry can. Gasoline was shimmering just below the fill-hole. He'd drained maybe a quarter of my tank. Before I could protest he was thrusting Deutschmarks at me.

"Molim! Hvala!"

I took the cash, saw that it was payment enough — generous, in fact.

"My car is not close. You are driving me please."

"Driving you? I have to get to Dubrovnik."

"Super! My car is same way."

I'd been conned, but I found it hard to sustain a sense of injury. I still had enough gas to reach Dubrovnik. Hariz hoisted his gas can into the back of the Golf. He was in the passenger seat before I'd finished fussing. When we were under way, I asked if Podgorica was his home.

"*Ne.* Sjenica."

"Within Sandjak, yes?"

He looked at me curiously. "Sandjak. You know?"

"I live here, near Priječko."

"Why you live there?"

"I had a friend. He was born in Priječko, or nearby."

"Name?"

"Pimm. Pimm Hoekstra."

"No one from Priječko has this name."

"His birth name was Saša Kožić."

"Why is he changing name?"

"He was adopted — *usvojio.* His parents died when he was a baby. He grew up in Canada."

"Is lucky for him."

"Yes. We are very lucky. Hariz, you are Muslim, yes?"

"Of course!"

"And Saša, this name is ..."

"Serb, Croat ..."

"Possibly Muslim?"

"Possible. In city. But not village Muslim."

"A Yugoslav name."

"*Sta? Ne.* 'Yugoslav' is meaning nothing. No name is 'Yugoslav.' Saša means ... it means Saša must only say what he is."

"What about Slobodan? Isn't that a Yugoslav name?"

"Is ... what you say ... is name for liberty."

"Freedom."

"Freedom, okay. But Chris, please, where is freedom? Where is Yugoslav freedom? Excuse, but ... Slobodan, he is bad fucking joke on us."

"Alright. Yes."

"Saša, he is from Priječko?"

"He was born there."

"Okay, so he is Serb, nine-nine percent chance."

"He's Canadian. He never lived in Yugoslavia except for eight months."

"His blood is Serb."

"Do you believe in blood, Hariz?"

He looked squarely at me.

"What believe? I bleed is Muslim blood."

"But under Tito —"

"Tito is dream. Long dream. Now we are awake."

A pause, the road unwinding before us.

"Were you raised in Sjenica, Hariz?"

"My family always living in Sjenica."

"Are there Kožić families there?"

"Possible. It is big town. Peoples are four zero ... *hiljada*."

"Forty thousand."

"Yes."

My Kožić question had been reflex. Kožićs were my multiplying ghosts. I glanced at Hariz. Sun angled into the car and gave his beard stubble a glint like copper wire. His hands rested on his thighs, thick veins under a patina of ginger hair. He looked at me.

"You living Canada or here?"

"I've been living here over two years."

"You go home now?"

"Just for a visit, a few weeks."

After a moment Hariz spoke to the windshield.

"Why you are living in Serbia? Nothing here. Nothing for ... *budućnost.*"

"For the future."

"Yes, is nothing. Maybe I go Canada. I am liking name! Go ka-nada."

He was punning; "ka nada" translated roughly as "toward hope."

He took out a pack of cigarettes.

"Is that wise?"

"Wise?"

"The gas fumes — *benzin.*"

"I open window."

"Okay. I guess. Open it wide."

We continued in silence, the Golf's heater fighting blasts of icy air. I might have queried him more, but I didn't want to probe Hariz's traumas. Whatever they were, Serbs would be the per-petrators. With hardly a thought of it, I'd also refrained from mentioning Strastanica. My intimacy with Serb monks would only prove my dismissal of Muslim lives. Priječko alone made my sympathies instantly suspect, but Hariz had let that go. We'd left things unspoken, preserving a functional goodwill.

Reading Slobo gave me the stories that others were too numb or too wise to dredge up. Perhaps Sjenica had been spared the divisions of other places and Hariz had not suffered directly. In any case, we would reach his car soon; our encounter was almost over. I began to wonder how much farther it could be. Slush fanned away from the tires as we eased around hairpins and down steep grades. Hariz's foot drummed impatiently on the floorboard. At a bend he sat forward.

"I think here is place."

His car was barely off the road, hard against a fall of rocks at the base of a sheer wall. It was a Golf. I pulled to a stop behind it and we got out.

"You had a long walk."

"I think to Žabljak. But you save me."

Like mine, Hariz's Golf was probably one of the thousands that had entered the black market from a huge Bosnian warehouse shortly after Serb occupation. His had survived what appeared to be a front-ender into a post. The bumper was bowed like a boomerang, the hood sprung on its hinges. In the back seat were three plastic crates full of videotapes. He climbed behind the wheel and cranked the starter, then gave up as the battery weakened.

"*Ništa.*"

"*Naravno!* Unless you were dreaming."

"Thank you for joke."

Hariz was a less canny, less prosperous version of Vuk. His conversation was genuine, none of Vuk's rolling patter. We got the gas into his tank and I insisted on returning a few Deutschmarks to him. The drive would be a favour, it was not in the least out of my way. He briskly declined. As he was cranking the motor again I reached in and put some bills on his dash. He ignored them, staring darkly ahead at the road and swearing elaborately as he wore down his battery. I watched his battle with pride and futility, an icy wind whistling down my neck.

"Hariz, maybe your gas line is blocked."

"*Ne.*"

"Or perhaps the fuel pump?"

"*Nije moguće.*"

"I have cables."

"Jumper cables?"

"Yes."

"Get please!"

I manoeuvered my car into position and took the cables from the trunk. There was little traffic on this road, but it struck me as odd that no one had stopped to assist Hariz. Perhaps he'd been too proud to flag someone down — until he saw me, a sitting duck. He seemed not quite a stranger now, and I wanted to see him through this. I still had time to reach Dubrovnik before evening. If Hariz's car resisted all coercion I could at least take him as far as Nikšić, along with his porn tapes.

The cables didn't advance our cause. Hariz had me engage the starter while he poked at the engine. My returned Deutschmarks rested on the dash like the insult I should have known they were. Then he came round and motioned me out with a smug smile, as if he'd just rigged our escape. When he turned the key there was now only a buzzing click. Again he persisted, swearing on mothers' pussies. I caught a scent of burning electrics.

"Hariz, I will take you to Nikšić. You can get a tow truck."

"*Lopovi!*"

"I think my cables are getting hot."

"*Minut, minut.*"

"May I shift your cargo?"

"*Čekaj.*"

He got out and went round to the engine, stared at it, poked again at the wiring.

"Hariz, I have to go soon, I have an appointment."

"Okay. Okay. I accept ride."

"Wonderful."

"*Kola nisu ni za kurac!*"

His car, he said, was not even worth being fucked. He began to kick its already smashed grill, and continued with dogged savagery until broken plastic littered the ground and it broke free of its mounts. He wrenched off a hanging piece and flung it hard against the rock wall a few metres away. Shrapnel flew back at us. He turned, grinning like a football hero, and punched his fist in the air: "Fuck all Germans!" He moved to the back seat to remove his goods. I reached in the front window and retrieved my Deutschmarks from the dash. As we drove off he asked if I liked pornography.

"I give you video. Sample."

"I don't have a VCR."

"I give you phone number. Mujo is the good friend. He is selling VCR cheap. Good porno too. Russian. Not raping. Girls get money."

I'd heard there were tapes circulating of group rapes and other atrocities in Bosnia. I had little interest in heterosexual porn, hardly more in gay porn, and certainly no use for a VCR, but I accepted Hariz's friend's number. The sample tape I declined, pleading the gauntlet of Croatian customs.

Chapter Twenty-two

I checked into the Hotel Lastovo, showered, changed, and went directly to the bar in a corner of the cavernous lobby. At seven I descended a floating Lucite staircase to the vast amber-lit dining room, containing only three diners. Toni had advised me that Martin had a "shock" of grey hair. There it was, at a table by the windows, angled toward a menu.

"Martin?"

He looked up.

"Chris."

He half-rose, stuck his hand out. He was maybe fifty, a tight smile, neutral grey eyes, his hair silver-grey, thick and wiry, curling over his ears. Paternally handsome. He nipped at what seemed to be a hefty Scotch.

"You need a drink."

"I'm okay, just came from the bar. Is that actually Scotch?"

"It's Zadar sherry."

"How is it?"

"Sweet. Just scanning the wine list here. I didn't do too well last night."

"Do they have a Dingač?

He ran his finger down.

"Yes. 'Peljesački.'"

"That's it. Toni introduced me to it."

"Well, Toni would know. Are you seeing her in New York?"

"She's putting me up. How's Slobo doing?"

"Okay. He sleeps a lot, goes under for a few days, then he climbs out of it and starts pounding out new stuff. I finally scrounged some fresh ribbons for him. Toni will be happy. Things opened up a little in Sarajevo this summer but it hasn't held. Same bullshit, one fake ceasefire after another, can't even figure out who's breaking them. At least we don't have Hot-Rod McKenzie out there playing favourites. Sorry, are you Canadian?"

"I am and you don't have to be sorry. Are you going back?"

"Got to. Slobo's a *Times* exclusive. He's in somewhat less danger now, or lately — they seem to have stopped targeting the hospital. Not worth the bad press."

"You must be glad to be out of there."

"Nice to have a break. But you get used to the tension. I'm home for Christmas, see the kids — 'kids,' they're in college for chrissake — then I'm back first week of January. But it's my call now, going back — there's no pressure from the *Times*. I was kind of surprised at the amount of damage here in Dubrovnik. I mean, I'd heard the rumours, but ... Actually, once you're out of the Old Town, you know, it looks a lot like Sarajevo. Except the rubble is in neater piles. And no one's getting killed. It's quiet. Too quiet. I'm waiting for the shells to come in. So where's your monastery?"

"Sandjak. Near the Bosnian border."

"Toni said you're funding some kind of restoration."

"Not quite. I've donated some money."

"Have you thought of restoring mosques instead?"

"All right, but where do you begin? Strastanica still has damage from World War II."

"People will say you're soft on the Serbs."

"I don't see that my Serbs, my monks, are guilty of anything."

"Why have you been there for — what is it, two years?"

"I just stayed. I guess I've become a hermit."

"You'd have to be."

"Monks are hermits who like company — just highly restricted company."

"Are you — what do they call it — a novice?"

"I'm a lay member. Officially, I'm on a religious visa."

"Don't you get a little squirrelly?"

"I'm busy, actually, singing, tending the garden, other things. We farm our own food."

Martin eyed me dubiously. He leaned in, the fruity sherry wafting on his breath.

"Toni said you're involved with the choirmaster."

"Oh, Christ."

"No, I think it's great. It's classic. I mean you'd need something like that. You have to get involved at some point, you know, corporeally."

The waiter appeared with food for the other diners, two men in dark suits. Martin signalled to him.

"I'd go with the squid. They grill it with lots of garlic, got a kind of casseroled rice thing on the side, not bad. Care for a shot of brandy to start?"

"Why not."

He ordered for us in smooth Serbo-Croat.

"So these monks, are they neutral, or what? How do they work it? I mean you're pretty close to the action there aren't you?"

"What do you mean, neutral? Some of them have family in Sarajevo."

"Sorry to hear it."

"The abbot considers Karadžić a criminal."

"What does he think of the bishop in Pale?"

"Martin, you know as well as I do."

"What do I know?"

"They might be old classmates. They could be brothers."

"Ouch. Are they?"

"I wouldn't ask."

"Good call."

"I have a favour to ask. I brought a few names and addresses. No pressure, of course, but when you go back ..."

"You want to know if they're okay. I'll do what I can."

"Thank you. I know it may be impossible."

"Depends."

"Not all of them are one hundred percent Serb."

"If you think that surprises me —"

"I just want you to know. We're actually sheltering two Muslim boys in the monastery, or part Muslim. Their parents died in Zvornik. Our choirmaster is their uncle."

"Your boyfriend."

"If you insist, Martin, yes."

"I think it's great. Wonderful."

"How would you know?"

"I wouldn't. What's his name?"

"Stefan."

Our slivovitz arrived. Martin toasted; we drank to Stefan, then to Slobo. The men nearby turned and stared at us, chewing. Martin quickly reiterated:

"Slobodan Kušić! *Pjesnik mira!*"

Poet of peace. The Croats turned again to their dinners. Martin sat back and sighed.

"Too many Slobos. How long are you staying with Toni?"

"A week or so."

"I'm coming in Thursday, three or four days. Give me a buzz when you know your schedule."

He wrote a number on his card. I stuck it in my wallet, next to Derek Andover's. I asked Martin if he knew him.

"Hell yes. He's in Sarajevo. He's had the same room at the Holiday Inn for two years. How do you know him?"

"We had a few drinks once. He's apparently won a bunch of awards."

"He's good. But too fucked up frankly, I mean way more than the rest of us. Got to be right in the thick of it with bullets flying or he feels half dead. He'd be shooting the breeze with you in your room, and if the shelling started he'd run across the hall and hang out in one of the wrecked rooms there, just watching the show. He had a sheet hung up on the balcony with viewing holes cut in it. He's fucking nuts, really. The plummy accent fools people. He likes looking at corpses. Yeah, see, this is a dividing thing. Some guys start looking for more. More blood. You know, bigger jolts. Andover had videos, Serb propaganda videos that he played in his room. He reported on all this horrific propaganda, did it brilliantly. But you'd wander into his room — we all left our doors open unless we were screwing or something — and he'd have these tapes running with the sound off. Pictures of people with their insides spilling out and, well, I can't tell you, incredible stuff. You'd be chatting with him and he'd have one eye on the TV. Like he didn't want to miss his favourite parts."

"That's just charming."

"Yeah. He did some interviews in the hospital. Slobo disliked him right from the get-go."

"I have a question, about Slobo's brother. The one born in 1945."

"Saša."

"Did Slobo ever mention the mother's name?"

"Not that I recall."

"Might it be Ljiljana?"

"Don't know. Could be, I guess. What's up?"

"Just a hunch. A family connection."

"You're related to Slobo?"

"It's possible."

"What do you need to know?"

"The mother's name would be a big help. First and last. If it's Ljiljana Kožić, then I think that would clinch it."

"Kožić? Saša's name is Kušić."

"Maybe. If Davor married her."

"Right. Well ... I'll try to find out. Write down the spelling for me."

The food came and we tucked in. Martin kept my wineglass filled.

"You have a family at home?"

"Cousins. I never see them. My friend Axel would like me to come home. But I'm starting to feel home is Strastanica."

"With Stefan."

"Yes. Though it's problematic."

"I guess it would be."

"He's a true believer."

"How true? As in Muslims can't go to heaven?"

"I doubt he believes that. We haven't discussed it."

"Well, you don't have to. Lots of people have crazy ideas they don't talk about. It can save marriages actually."

"We do talk about belief, faith. I'm intrigued by his certainty. And I have regular tasks there, obediences. They're very accommodating and generous, in a remote kind of way."

"But you don't believe."

"Not in Jesus, no."

"Is problem."

"Stefan's words exactly. I don't know what to do about it except ... let it run its course."

"Won't they boot you at some point if you don't commit?"

"They might. But we don't — Stefan and I, we don't ..."

"Screw?"

"Anymore. It was only a few times. And he had a crisis. It had to stop."

"No one found out?"

"I don't know. Stuff goes on that isn't revealed. There's selective silence. And despite the cramped situation, there's privacy. It's a lot like a family that way, people who live together and ignore each other."

Martin gazed at me, then, it seemed through me.

"I don't mesh with family. Not for long. I can give it a good shot, then I've got to get out, get on a plane. I live alone and I like it. As long as I'm busy."

"You don't get lonely?"

"No. I get bored."

"Axel's like that. Too busy for romance."

"Well, see, this is what's good about war zones in general. There's a lot happening, high personnel turnover, and sex is a stress release — I mean if there's some running water and you don't have to wear a coat indoors. This summer I had a little thing going with a gal from Sydney. Twenty-eight years old."

"A thing?"

"She's in Somalia now. This wasn't romance you understand. And I've never been with Toni, in case you're wondering."

Martin didn't show for breakfast next morning. I was glad simply to eat in silence, nursing my delicate head. Back upstairs as I was packing up, a knock came at the door.

"Glad I caught you. You'll be seeing Toni before I do. Would you mind passing this on to her? A new instalment from Slobo. There's an interview too, might interest you."

Chapter Twenty-three

14/11/94

Toni:

Here's Slobo in conversation. The *Times* isn't running it as a Q&A, so I thought you'd like the uncut version. We spoke in the hospital garden in September. Beautiful day, people out in the sun. Heard the trams clattering down on Maršala Tita. No serious shelling for over a month at that point, but it broke that afternoon. Anyway we got in a good chat. The translation is mine, two months working on and off. I was humbled. Next time it's yours. Slobo turned 63 this week. The nurses gave him a little party, minus cake and candles. He got a tin of sardines and, from me, a little airline bottle of Johnnie Walker.

    Martin

Martin Ivry: You've been in Kostreša Hospital for eight months.
    How was it that you found yourself, in January of this year,
    in an abandoned truck near Sarajevo Airport?

Slobodan Kušić: I didn't find myself in the truck. I chose to stay there. It was quite warm actually. It had a little gas heater. For water I melted snow. For food I had a large bag of instant potato flakes that I took from the back of a U.N. vehicle. I stole it, in fact. But I was in need, and the convoy was stopped at a roadblock. They saw me moving away with it but they did nothing because they had Serb guns pointed at their chests. They all swore at me. The Serb militia and the U.N. people. The Serbs wanted the food as well. The Serb curses were of course more illustrious. But they didn't give chase. I looked sufficiently pathetic.

MI: How long were you in the truck?

SK: Perhaps a few weeks. Nobody bothered me. I ate warm mashed potato. I slept. Everything was simple. I was a harmless old man in a wrecked truck. Then someone came and siphoned my gas tank, and so I began eating snow and dry potato flakes, and then they came and brought me here, where they also had no fuel, so it was no warmer than the truck. They told me I was delusional, dehydrated, depressed, and I suppose I was some of those. But now they say my writing is the best therapy. They can't obtain the usual drugs.

MI: How did you end up in Sarajevo?

SK: I was placed under guard, in the autumn, by the commander of a Serb checkpoint near Podromanija. They brought me with some others to a house where I was held for a few days and asked some questions, and I tried my best to be only a dithering old man. They thought I might be a threat to the security of the Bosnian Serb people. I escaped the house one night in the confusion of a raid.

MI: But you are part Serb, are you not?

SK: Part, yes. If I'm to be called only one thing it might be a Bosnian, or an ex-Yugoslav. I'm a person of ambiguous alliance — my papers confirm it. A bad thing to be during a blood war. But we must put quotation marks around the blood. It's real enough blood, but of course there's no difference between all these bloods. It's like a vast auto-immune disease. The body is eating itself. And the rest of the world is savouring the leftovers on the television news. Sometimes they make a face at the bitter taste. But they can feel blessed. God has spared them the particular disease, so far.

MI: This interview might become part of the news. Do you want that?

SK: Like everyone, I hope, perhaps vainly, to have an influence. I suppose I trust you, more or less.

MI: Thank you.

SK: But I have my guard up. Somebody filmed me two years ago in my village. I wasn't at my best. My clothing was torn and bloodied, and I was not quite coherent because, well, in the night I had lost my house to some boys who were having fun burning houses and smashing heads, raping if they could, but most of the women and children were gone by then. A TV news crew came through. I was a victim for their camera before I could even say hello or ask who they were. A bit later I saw them filming fresh wooden crosses in the graveyard. The man with the microphone looked so regretful. He was deeply saddened. I learned later in Sarajevo that this image was broadcast across the world as a report on Muslim war victims. They didn't even know that Muslims do not erect crosses over their dead! The crosses were Serbian, with Serbian names on them. Just around the bend along the river road was a Muslim village that had been burnt to the ground, and fresh Muslim graves. The TV people recorded a fantasy, and then they got into their vehicles and drove blindly past the reality they had been seeking, past the graves that would have better served the half-truths they were intent on reporting. In retrospect, I began to feel the enormity of this farce.

MI: That is the subject of your "history," as you call it.

SK: Yes, well, I call it that, but it's something else. War must be understood as a game of falsehoods and epic manipulations. Also of absurd and unaccountable events, things that must be denied or explained away lest their truth be discovered. Always the subtext is more interesting, if one can read it. The manuscript is also, for me, an attempt to keep my head from pounding and spinning. It gathers my thoughts. I think, really, that I prefer thought to feeling. Feeling overwhelms me. My feelings have been overstimulated.

MI: Tell me more about your home village, Mali Voćnjak. It was predominantly Serb?

SK: The census of 1991 put Serbs at eighty-some percent. The village council was entirely Serb. Our Muslims were shopkeepers, tradespeople. One was a doctor, she birthed many Serb children. Now the village is a ruin with many dead, some Muslims living in the serviceable Serb houses, and those Serbs are themselves dead or living in abandoned houses somewhere else. The Yugoslav housing exchange. My childhood village was Serb and Croat and Muslim, until Chetniks and Ustashas came and fought over it, and then Partisans.

MI: Who burned your house?

SK: My childhood house? My father said it was Ustashas, the Croatian Fascists.

My house in Mali Voćnjak was burned by Muslim soldiers, one of whom my daughter had gone to school with. They were boys in ragtag uniforms who were self-licensed as avenging angels. Or some of them just relished the idea of creating, you know, a little circle of hell so they could see what it looked like. They took my neighbour, Mihajlo, who was near seventy, and they simply shot him in the face. They were drunk enough to do that. Mika was a good neighbour. We each lived alone in our house, the houses we ourselves built thirty, forty years ago. We drank brandy and coffee together. On the day he was shot I was sleeping, because it was impossible to sleep at night, they were firing guns in the night, all night, and tearing around in their rusty Zastavas with no mufflers. Then it would be quiet from dawn until the early afternoon. They had taken the town days before. There were no Serb fighters left to challenge them, only unburied corpses. Their surviving enemy amounted to only a handful of old people in broken down houses, the few who were too sick or too stubborn to abandon their homes.

I woke up to repeated shots. I went to the window and saw Mika's body slumped on the porch behind his house. His head was a mass of blood. The killers were in his house swearing and laughing, looking, I suppose, for more brandy to steal. But now they could steal other things, or just move in for a few days until the provisions were gone, and they had fully ruined the interior so that it was unlivable, filling the corners with shit and so on, shooting the walls, pissing on the carpets. Having shot an old granddad, their laughter was especially sharp and angry. They were in that fit of alcoholic anger that, with the scent of blood all around, and easy killing, passes for elation. It is played out as a kind of super-charged happiness. The joy of full power. But really, to me, they always seem to exist at a fever pitch of misery. They want to be at home, waiting for mother's feast to appear on the table, but mother is either dead or in flight and home is a charred ruin. Or they want, really, to be shooting the Chetnik who raped their sister, or the father who beat them, or the bully who tormented them in school. But they don't know what they want. They know that bearing arms raises them from defeat and makes them strong, and that killing makes them men. They think that a man is someone who has mastered pain, who can cause pain while never feeling it. But they do feel it, and kill it. And so on.

MI: Were you a victim of these militias?

SK: They harassed me, but I was not truly abused until they destroyed my house. My regular visits with Mika came to their attention, and this marked me finally as more Serb than Muslim, regardless of my birth and marriage papers or the number of Muslim artifacts displayed in my house, which was not many. I was not especially religious. I was in between everything. I have always been in between every-thing, even as a child. A universal suspect. Still they could not bring themselves to shoot the son of a Muslim mother. But they could shoot my friend, my neighbour, and when I came with an old sister of his to take his body away in a wheelbarrow for burial they swore at us. Some days later they dragged me from my house, kicked and beat me and lobbed grenades into my house, and it burned. The next morning the TV people came while the Rambos were still passed out in their brandy comas and I was picking through the smoking debris of my house, and they asked me if I was Muslim. But I wasn't Muslim enough for them either.

MI: Has there been a point in your life when it didn't matter whether you were one thing or another?

SK: As a child it seemed that way. School was in one room. The high school was at Sjecišta and students would walk there each day from the surrounding villages. We all went to the same school except some who might eventually go to a religious school in one of the towns. But I was in school only four years when the war broke out.

MI: In which, I recall, your parents were killed?

SK: My mother was murdered by Chetniks in 1941, just after the Fascist occupation, the excuse being that Muslims in Sjecišta region were collaborating with the Ustashas. A Muslim mother might, for instance, be transporting weaponry between villages, under the vegetables in her shopping basket. My parents' marriage was rare. Everyone knew she had Muslim blood. In wartime it doomed her. The loss compelled father to join the Partisans. He was later killed in Montenegro. My sister and I spent the war years with an aunt and uncle, both dead now.

MI: Is your sister living?

SK: Vedrana lives in Belgrade. She became ill, a lymphoma, but treatable. She is in good care, the last I had news.

MI: And you mentioned a brother I think?

SK: A half-brother. I've not seen him for fifty years.

MI: Is he presumed dead?

SK: I can presume nothing. I don't know. He was born to a woman my father met near the end of the war. I saw her with Father only once, for a day or two. He must have been on leave. He was quite dashing. I was stricken. He had a cap with the red star on it. I remember he was very affectionate with this woman, more so than I'd ever seen him with Mother. He may have married her, but I don't recall a wedding. Father returned to the fighting and was killed. Vedrana and I were living then with Aunt's mother in Priboj, in Serbia, and after the war ended the woman came to visit us with a baby. She told me that the child was my little brother, named Saša, after my father's father. She took photos with a box camera and later on we got some pictures. I remember her nursing him, sitting in the shade behind the house. I could only think, How can a little brother of mine be at the teat of this stranger? I've not seen them since. Aunt said they went to America.

MI: And your daughter, where is she now?

SK: I've not spoken to Zlata for almost two years. They were planning a move to Skopje where her husband had found work, but I've been unable to reach her. I might even have grandchildren now, but I don't know.

(At this point a bombardment began — explosions downtown, then a shell hit the municipal building downhill from the hospital. We took shelter. MI)

Two Sašas. Kušić and Kožić. Born spring or summer of 1945 in the Priječko-Priboj area. Each fatherless. Each left the country with his mother. I had some more questions for Martin. When I phoned down to reception I learned that he'd checked out.

I had to hustle to make my plane. In the taxi I reread the close of the interview. Slobo recalled Saša's mother clearly. Maybe he remembered her name. And there were photos. Were they pictures of baby Pimm? Where were they now? As we surged into the air over Dubrovnik I had my flight bag open on my lap and was twisting the lid from the rigid tube that held Pimm's birth certificate. I gently unrolled it and read the name Љиљана Кожић — Pimm's mother, Ljiljana Kožić. Kušić would be Кушић in Cyrillic. I took a pencil and a stick-on note from my bag and posted my handwritten Кушић next to the official Кожић. I stared at the smudged typewritten letters on the certificate. The central "ж" in Кожић was a solid squarish blotch. Why had we assumed it was a "ж"? Because that matched the "ž" on the Italian adoption papers. The "ж" blotch could as easily be a "ш" blotch, making the name on the certificate Košić. That would leave only the "o" as the variable. So, a simple error at the registry office, turning Kušić to Košić. Eight months later an Italian clerk squinted at the Cyrillic blotch, and a second error completed the transformation. Saša Kušić became Saša Kožić. Or, much simpler, Ljiljana may have retained her maiden name, and Pimm was a Kožić all along. I stared at the letters. It was probably all a fantasy, an empty coincidence. Not much of a coincidence at all, in fact. There were many Sašas, even more war-dead fathers, thousands of wartime refugees. The stepmother's name would be the next piece to help solve the puzzle.

A voice interrupted my thoughts.

"*Da li tragate za nestalima iz vaše obitelji, porodice?*"

The elderly woman next to me was looking calmly into my face. She'd asked if I was searching for missing family, offering both Croat and Serb variants for "family." I confirmed that I was.

She said she'd lost a grandson in the 1991 war. For the rest of the short flight she was silent, except to press upon me some dried figs, *iz mog vrta*, from her garden.

Part Two

Chapter Twenty-four

A delay in Zagreb stretched my travel time by hours, landing me at Kennedy after midnight. Toni met me at the airport and we sailed into Manhattan on rainy but unclogged highways. Her Riverside apartment offered a sidelong view of the skyline stretching all the way down to the Twin Towers. She soon had me settled on the couch, sipping Scotch that tasted foreign.

"How's Martin?"

"He seems eager to get back to the war."

"Amazing isn't it."

"He got me quite drunk, grilled me about the monastery."

"I mentioned Stefan — hope you don't mind."

"I think it gave him a thrill. He was practically thumping me on the back. I brought a new Slobo instalment for you — a thick one."

"I've heard. Did Martin mention an interview?"

"I've got that too."

"It was in the *Times* last week. What do you think?"

"I think that Pimm might be Slobo's brother."

"Um ... try that again?"

"The half-brother. You should read the transcript. He had the same name as Pimm, was born spring or summer 1945 in Priboj area, father absent or dead. And they both left Yugoslavia with their mother."

"Same name?"

"Saša. Kožić and Kušić."

Toni stared at me, a complicated stare, mixed with surprise, scepticism and cool appraisal. She started to speak but I rode over her.

"I know Saša's a common name. But we know Kožić isn't. The Cyrillic isn't clear on the birth certificate. Pimm might have been a Kušić."

"Where was he born?"

"Priječko. About twenty kilometres from Priboj. Slobo saw his baby brother Saša at Priboj, just after Pimm's birth."

"That's ... interesting."

"I'm hoping Slobo will know the stepmother's name. Pimm's mother was Ljiljana."

"Another common one."

"But if they share it ..."

"If Slobo remembers. He met her once?"

"Twice. She took photos in Priboj too, baby pictures. When I go back the first thing would be to try and clarify the family name with the registry office."

"Where's that?"

"Rudačac. In Bosnia."

"Then I guess you're out of luck."

"It's on the border. It's been a Serbian town for two years."

"A Serbian town? Have they moved the border?"

"No."

"So it's a Bosnian town, full of Serbs."

"Yes. Obviously."

"So you can't just go in. You'd probably need a U.N. pass for starters. Would the office even be functional? Try to phone them or get an address or something. Maybe you can send a copy of the documents."

"That makes sense."

"You don't want to be wandering around some Chetnik military base."

"Toni, what do think Prije\u010dko is?"

"Prije\u010dko is a Serbian town."

Martin was due in on Thursday. With Toni busy at Columbia and Axel stuck in Toronto with work, I was more or less on my own for three days. New York began to demonstrate how alien I'd become. As rain turned to dry, frigid bluster I cabbed between museums and galleries, seeking any place that offered a haven from the car horns, the traffic, the strangers thronging the sidewalks. I had dinner with Derek and Kent in the Village and watched their faces flicker with incomprehension as I tried to evoke Strastanica in some way that didn't seem defensive. Later in their apartment they tanked me up on Dalwhinnie and I got talking about Stefan. They were rapt. My story was about illicit lust, secret romance. But their eyes still had that glaze of incredulity. My new life was unexplainable.

First thing Thursday morning, I left Martin a message asking if he knew anything additional about Slobo's childhood in Priboj. Then I set out for Central Park, leaving Toni in the shower and fresh coffee brewing in the kitchen. The day was sunny, the park kinetic with cyclists and runners and roller-bladers. I passed a phalanx of men with leaf-blowers, then a machine that sucked up and digested tree branches. The noise was soul-rattling. Skirting the reservoir, I aimed for the Russian Orthodox Cathedral at 5th and 97th. Through the trees I caught sight of the spike and gilded cross of its dome.

At 8:30 a young priest opened the doors. A hunched granny and a florid man with a briefcase moved ahead of me to kiss the icons. The man quickly lit a candle and left, trailing cologne. The granny, bewigged and lost in her furs, hovered before the reliquary. I stood taking in the icons. A Christ in oils hung grace-fully on a cross, a pensive Mary opposite. Craning my neck, I stared up into a blue bowl scattered with gilt stars. The granny lit her candles — about a dozen of them. I thought I might, for once, light the full roster myself, but ended by reprising my Strastanica routine: one candle for Pimm, and one for all the sick and dead I didn't wish to tally. I dropped a bill into the box and went back out into the din.

At the Metropolitan Museum sunlight had cleared the apart-ment towers and was gracing the upper steps by the museum entrance. In the 1970s I'd sat on those steps with Pimm. We'd discovered early on that we could not do museums together. He couldn't stand before a painting or a Greek vase for more than a few moments. While I lingered, he was always drifting on, seeking the next room. He needed people and events — if not actual motion, then talk, or plot. Novels could satisfy him, but not potboilers. He had an ongoing affair with Henry James. A maroon hardcover of *The Ambassadors* sat for years by his chair in the living room. Every so often he'd pick it up and re-enter. On other nights he'd be out on the prowl, seeking James's deeply buried subtexts.

Later on, when he couldn't read (or prowl) I read the book aloud to him, and I often felt I got the rhythms wrong, lost the nuance of those sinuous, gathering sentences. But he didn't complain. Just lay there with his brow knitting now and then.

From the beginning Pimm had the longer, more practical view. Partway through graduate school it occurred to him that reading books was not a career. When we met he was thirty and steadily employed in banking. He hardly ever talked about work. Toward the end he seemed mostly to have lunch with other bankers. I was the one who, beset by students, came home with stories of my day. I'd stayed with the books, pummelling teenagers with my eccentric views on Dickens and Atwood and Dostoyevsky. In Pimm's final months I nearly finished out the year. But I couldn't go back in September. The only thing I could do then was feel robbed and poisoned. I could stomach no company but Axel's, and his only barely. Axel raised me from the abyss.

In New York I'd browse through the galleries or spend hours, entire afternoons, surveying the throngs on 5th Avenue from the steps of the Metropolitan Museum. Pimm and Axel would meet friends for lunch over white linen at tony places east of the Park, knocking back gin and Chardonnay among the idle-rich matrons. Then they would shop — usually for clothes, which could be sported through customs. At seven we'd all meet at Julius, or The Monster, where the piano was, and we'd get tanked to the strains of Gershwin, Cole Porter, Sondheim, even *A Chorus Line* and Streisand — we could get giddy enough to succumb to those too. Then we'd roll out to a dinner passed in a fog of delirium lit with powder-flashes of rude wit.

Of eight steady friends in New York, two died before Pimm, Bernard after. The Toronto deaths, from a much larger social set, are an untallied blur. Avoiding the unthinkable, the idea of losing Pimm, I also avoided the deaths of others. The care teams and funerals and memorials, the tears and hugs and eulogies became a numbing round of duty while I withheld my real lament. The New York circle was tighter; it came in concentrated, memorable doses, and so became dearer to us. Time in New York was party time. In Toronto we worked and cocooned, and let friendships drift untended.

I was among a handful admitted when the Metropolitan opened its doors at nine. The cavernous galleries were deserted. Favourite things (the Temple of Dendur, the Greek sculptures) spurred a drowsy déjà vu. Standing before a youth's marble torso, I scanned for guards, then cupped the curve of cool buttock in my palm. It felt as real as ever, but the reference points had shifted. I recalled chilly evenings in the guest quarters at Strastanica.

A little later I was standing in front of St. Sava Cathedral on 26th Street. It had the look of St. Paul's in Toronto. A bronze plaque explained that Manhattan Serbs had been worshipping in a reconsecrated Episcopal church for fifty years. Inside, oak pews receded before me to a carved and gilded altar screen. Sun spilled through Gothic windows to pool at the feet of icons.

The only other worshipper was a tall beak-nosed man in a raincoat. A caretaker entered from a side door and scanned the burning tapers, straightening some, snuffing others that were spent. He moved past us down the centre aisle and threw me a vaguely wary glance. (I'd been told early on by Vuk that I could never be mistaken for a Serb. My head was Teutonic, he said, my nose Irish.)

I moved back down the narrow aisle to the rear and found the caretaker by the entrance, arranging his size-graded candles and incense and souvenir Saints. I stopped and caught his eye, and asked in Serbian if I could sit for a moment. I knew there was no need to ask. The need was to connect myself to him and to the place. I slid onto a wooden bench, sat taking in the long view of timbered arches framing the distant shimmer of Byzantium.

I was due at Toshi's. I detoured through Washington Square, thinking I might buy some grass for him. Under hard sunlight, with grit and trash whirling in the cold wind, the square simply looked grim, the drug dealers and the homeless equally desolate. I was hindered by sensible fears of ripoff and arrest. I didn't even know the going rate for my vice.

I arrived at Toshi's cozy West 4th walk-up. Today's lunch had been shrewdly planned. We progressed through vodka and oysters to scallops, stir-fry and Beaujolais, then a kind of false langour on the couch, which led to a spirited tumble in fresh sheets. Toshi and I had discreetly flirted while Pimm and Bernard were alive. I hadn't known how serious he'd been. Now it was a fantastic release, grief ceding some of its power to pleasure. And there was homage in it too. When Toshi got out of bed he stood poised, staring at a framed photo on his dresser.

"I forgot to turn Bernie to the wall."

We agreed it was a positive step. Toshi was the first New York friend who hadn't blanched at my monk's beard. Bernard had been big and woolly, a real daddy bear.

Back at Toni's I found no sign of her, and no message from Martin. I lay back on the couch, thinking, Here I am, drunk before sunset and no plans for the evening. I thought about making herbal tea, and pictured the corner shelf at Strastanica, where boxed tea sits with mugs bearing pictures of wildflowers, each with its hovering bee. Coffee was available only at extortionate prices, or not at all. Drifting to sleep on Toni's couch, I made a mental note to buy some coffee and fancy teas for the brothers.

The ringing phone wakened me to darkness. Toni's machine kicked in and I heard, *Hi Toni, Martin Ivry here. I'm in for four days. Chris, I have no info about Priboj but I'll ask Slobo when I go back. Hope to see you both. Buzz me anytime.*

Chapter Twenty-five

Axel arrived the day before his birthday. When I opened the door of Toni's apartment he looked dumbstruck.

"My God, it's Raskolnikov!"

"Do you mean Rasputin?"

We embraced, letting the contact move through us. I shed a tear and Axel didn't, turning it to energy as he moved past me and into the kitchen, plunked his bag down and withdrew a bottle of Stolichnaya, then two video cassettes. I knew what the tapes were without asking: news footage from Bosnia. Axel rested his hand on them.

"Keep these. I'd like your opinion on them at some point."

What he meant was: this is the stuff you won't get on RTS.

We sipped Bloody Marys in Toni's living room, taking in our renewed presence, noting the novelty of being at a loss for words. But the air wasn't empty.

"I confess I'm having some trouble with the facial hair. Do you think you might trim it? You could have a smart goatee. I'll do it for you right now. Like Stefan's — doesn't he have a goatee?" Axel couldn't resist the impulse to make me presentable.

We found scissors in Toni's bathroom. As my reflection edged closer to an image of Stefan, I saw that what made him look trim and handsome made me look fussily professorial. I called for a reassessment. Axel clipped me down to stubble, produced shave foam and a blade from his bag, and I razored my face bare. Blood seeped from tiny wounds. When we walked out for lunch the air shocked my white chin.

Axel's birthday was Saturday. I suggested I'd like to treat him and Toni to a joint dinner, but Axel insisted on one-on-one time.

"I've missed two years of birthdays with you. Yours and mine. Four birthdays. I don't want to share this one with Toni."

We were in a grocery dawdling near the checkout while Toni shopped for dinner. She approached with her cart and Axel turned to her.

"What's on the menu?"

"Veal. In a tarragon mascarpone cream sauce with a few drops of Frangelico."

"Wow. We won't expect that every night."

"You won't get it. I've got faculty dinners coming up. You boys need to catch up anyway. Show Chris some culture. Take him to see *Three Tall Women*, the reviews are over the top."

"Tom Stoppard!" I said. "What a treat."

They both gazed at me with pity.

"Albee," said Axel. "Ed-ward Al-bee. You've been under a rock too long."

At dinner, with a birthday boy's licence, Axel probed relentlessly about Stefan and my connection to him, to Strastanica, to the idea of God — though faith was far from his first concern.

"He's uncut?"

"Of course. They all are, except the twins."

"How would you know that?"

"Serbs have foreskins, Muslims don't."

"You make it sound genetic."

"It's fundamental. For Muslims it's about hygiene. But a Serb without a foreskin is diminished, he's half a man."

"You must be embarrassed in the showers."

"Nobody showers together. All that stuff is private. Stefan's the only one I've seen naked."

"Tell me about it."

"It?"

"The object itself."

"It's ... beautifully proportioned."

"Big?"

"I guess above average."

"Bigger than mine?"

"That would be difficult."

"Is he experienced?"

"He's talented. He's safety conscious. I wouldn't know how experienced he is."

"What about the handyman?"

"Petko. Well, I saw Petko wanking in the woods once."

"You said he services people."

"I don't really know. Everyone's quite circumspect. The walls are thick. And there's the guest building, off by itself."

"The local bordello."

"You don't understand. Evidence doesn't turn up. I've only seen it once. Once I was coming back from a hike and I saw Teodos heading up the hill from the guest quarters. He was doing what Stefan and I used to do, cutting up through the trees and coming back along the forest path, like he'd been out for a walk."

"Did he see you?"

"Yeah. He twitched a bit, and then he nodded hello, this little bowing nod we do for greeting. It was very ordinary, like nothing was really amiss, then he just went down the path ahead of me. You have to realize, when monks meet like that they don't start blathering away like us. Silence is the expected thing. It doesn't mean avoidance. It means harmony, in fact."

"Or appalling secrets."

"The appalling thing would be to accuse, to make it explicit."

"To break ranks."

"No. Just to betray. Anyway, Teodos went in through the kitchen ahead of me. Then I was standing by the door taking my boots off, and Petko came down the path from the guest building with his tool kit."

"Can I fix that for you, brother?"

"Precisely. But it's not proof. Not really."

"Close enough. Don't they have to flagellate themselves after something like that?"

"Stefan did. He was torn up by it."

"He was torn up because you cheated on him."

"Well, yes."

"You'd think the boss would catch on to this stuff."

"He might. So they do penance. Or if it got truly disruptive someone could be forced to leave. But Stefan wouldn't be forced out; he's the abbot's golden boy."

"It sounds like a hotbed of hypocrisy."

"Because we're talking about it. Nobody there talks about love or passion casually, or about sin or deceit. Not in conversation. And they don't do the Catholic confessional stuff. It's all in the liturgy. It happens in the church, or alone in people's rooms — save us, have mercy on us, teach us perfect love. I mean, listen, they're not perfect; they're as screwed up or not screwed up as any other group of twenty friends. Or family. They're not all repressed homosexuals either. That's just your lascivious mind at work."

"Having a boyfriend is not a sin."

"I know."

"So what are you doing with a boyfriend who thinks so?"

"Stefan's not my boyfriend."

"Of course he is."

"He's a friend."

"Who thinks that gay love is abominable."

"Not love. The real sin is sex, the corporeal stuff."

"That's a fucked-up viewpoint."

"All right, fine. But I don't even care if I have sex with Stefan now. Pimm and I had no sex for almost ten years, and it was insignificant, it was a non-issue. In fact, I would prefer not to have sex with Stefan again; it's just a problem. Who needs it? I don't."

Axel put his knife and fork down and looked straight into my eyes.

"Chris. Why are you there? It's been over two years."

"Obviously because of ... all the things we talked about. Reinvention, healing ..."

"What's the real reason?"

"I know it's hard to understand but —"

"Because you love Stefan. You're in love with him."

Axel's eyes flickered with triumph. Now I was the one to stop eating, while he resumed, sorting out my life between forkfuls of risotto.

"The God issue. How are you going to work that out?"

"We've talked about it."

"Is he wavering?"

"No."

"You sound very sure of that."

"He calls gay life a folly. That's the word he used."

"He's in denial. Totally."

"He's a monk."

"Where did he study music?"

"Belgrade."

"I wonder what happened there."

"He doesn't talk about the past."

"You're obviously not his first encounter."

"That's pretty clear, yes. But if he has a gay past he's obviously rejected it."

"And is Chris rejecting it too? I mean, that's what monks do don't they, reject the world, reject their former lives?"

Axel ate calmly, glancing at my face as though he'd asked if I wanted more wine.

"I'll always be part of the community, like you are, like we all are. We carry it with us don't we? At Strastanica it's me and Stefan and — God knows who else. Maybe no one. I think most monks, nuns, if they've found their peace, then sex goes to the bottom of the list. They're free of it."

"Tell me what's happening, Chris. If you're becoming a monk I'd find that a little bewildering. A lot bewildering."

"I can't believe in that sort of God."

"Well you're in a real fucking dilemma then."

"It's not a dilemma."

"A limbo."

"No. A transition."

"So you have to go back."

"That was never in doubt."

"Okay. So go."

Axel's gaze went inward. He hunched his shoulders, frowning at his plate.

"You should come and visit the monastery."

"Yes. I will. I want to."

"Come in the summer. I'll meet you in Dubrovnik. Maybe Toni will join us. We can drive in through the mountains."

"Good. That sounds like fun."

"You can learn a little Serbian."

Axel eyed me.

"*Zašto?*"

"Because you wouldn't want any Croatian to sneak in, smart ass."

"There are no Croats in Sandjak?"

"Haven't met one yet."

"How would you know?"

"Context. We can stay a night or two at the Lastovo. Loosen you up for your Christian trial."

"Oh, God."

"Stefan will look at you like you're the devil. But wait till you hear him sing."

Over dessert Axel moved in for the kill.

"What exactly do you believe?"

"It's obvious there's something higher. Forces we don't understand."

"Particle physics."

"Beyond that. Maybe there's another way of existing."

"You mean an afterlife?"

"I don't think we should fear death."

"What about slow death? Like torture and AIDS and Alzheimer's and, you know, starved rats eating into your brain through your eyeballs. That stuff."

"We should fear that."

"Why does it happen?"

"You know the answer: 'Why not?'"

"Stefan would have an answer."

"His answer is that if we don't have an answer we haven't suffered enough."

"Is that why you're there? To suffer?"

"I haven't suffered there. I suffered in Toronto, in my own home. I thought I was going mad. I don't have to tell you that. In Strastanica I'm calm. I'm engaged. The war enters into it but ..."

"It's part of the engagement."

"Yes."

"And you're in a privileged position."

"Don't start."

Chapter Twenty-six

I have promised redemption. Let us now dispense with the depressing, the cruel, the unduly forthright, the million things we must veil in order to maintain our faith in life, love, a higher purpose. An uplifting episode will now unfold. Forget Spaso and his Kalashnikov and his devilish imagination. Hope that he stays far away. He is a brute hardly cognizant of the harm he wreaks. Remember instead our Great Hope, our Freedom Man, our Slobo. His purpose is our own. Renewed war has only toughened his resolve. In stirring broadcasts from the Belgrade Truth Network he reveals all murdering Spasos to be slanderous Western figments — or, if real, mere chicken thieves. Slobo reasserts our nobility before God and the West. And now see how he comes again in the flesh on a fresh spring morning in 1992, racing through pre-dawn clouds in thunderous return from the Bosnian border. Soon Belgrade will awaken to the sound.

The huge blades blur and tilt. The dark insect shape angles its blunt snout down the course of the stately Sava. Distant hotel towers and hulking government blocks are still in shadow, but high within the steel chariot the morning sun is already gracing our Great Leader's fine visage: the growing heft of jowl, the thrusting knob of chin, the astounding ear lobes, the anchoring hub of nose, the forehead of such polished amplitude that it is said pilots can navigate over all of Yugoslavia simply by bouncing their radar from it. And above it all, the hair, rising from the curved plain of cranium like the Montenegrin cliffs that trembled at his birth. And let us not forget the small yet piercing eyes, now pricked by tears as they catch the first glints of sun from the Victory Monument, the RTS transmission tower, the Orthodox Cathedral, and the Luxury International Hotel and Business Centre. (Admittedly there is another prick to the eye, an acrid and exhaustive one, present since departure, from the used motor oil in the smuggled Bulgarian gasoline that powers Slobo's chopper.)

The president will shortly alight onto the broad pavement fronting the International Hotel. He has been awake for hours, marshalling his thoughts for a crucial meeting with the skilled lackeys of Western governments. In the border town of Ratkovac he spent a full day drinking and sparring with a man of even more formidable coiffure: the great Radovan, whose name means joy. Freedom and Joy kissed as if brothers, clapped palms onto broad backs and commenced to pencil lines on the Bosnian map. In the fortified hilltop home of a lubricious militarist toady, the two Serb lions bared cordial teeth and struggled toward mutual advantage. The homemade *šljivovica* flowed. A pig slowly turned over a pit of coals. Rado argued fluently, downing brandy like water and tearing into hunks of pork, miming the pleasure and ease of an old friend. Slobo smiled and considered, injected his share of prurient wit, consumed moderately and excused himself at eleven. Banishing envious thoughts of Radovan's extravagant mane he fell into a satisfied sleep. This schemer was sly, but he was manageable.

Roused at five by his guard, Slobo groomed himself with his arsenal of foreign products. Ultra-Ban ensures that he is dry under the pressure of diplomacy. Pomade from the Upper Canada Hair and Skin Care boutique on Gavrilo Princip Street wafts a faint scent of lavender round the famous bristle. (Within a month, only hours after this shop closes its doors to honour U.N. sanctions, its last stocks of lavender pomade will be unaccountably confiscated and spirited away by Special Police in a black Mercedes.)

And now the president hovers over Belgrade. There is no crowd to greet him at the Luxury International. Indeed, not even the hotel management knows his manner of arrival. Police, carefully briefed, will quickly converge and clear the area in the minutes before landing, and Slobo will emerge without fanfare from his fuming bird, mere yards from the heavy glass doors of the lobby. Hotel staff and guests will gape and burst into spontaneous applause. All will succumb to the thrill of such blithe power and privilege, and our leader's legend will grow. When the chopper departs, the duly dazzled people will not see the import of its miasmic clouds.

Eight suited men accompany Slobo to the front desk. He moves as within a living fortress, each man a blockhouse of muscle and bone, each fingering a hard pistol within a pocket. It is said these pistols can stop a charging elephant at one hundred paces. Belgrade is rife with traitors and vermin, many of them bankrolled by the foreign conspiracy. Anyone foolish enough to take aim at our leader will find himself strewn across the plush lobby carpets.

Following a brief consultation with the hotel manager, the assemblage again moves as one to the elevators. Chrome doors slide open and Slobo boards with his first officer. The doors close and all eyes rise to the progress of winking numbers, confirming swift ascent to the presidential suite. When the figures freeze at twenty-one the manager steps forward to insert a small key into the elevator console. A quick turn of the hand secures Slobo's privacy until the day's first round of diplomacy, where he will expertly dissemble before the shrewd, indifferent or intransigent emissaries of nations who have the grace to scourge their enemies with greater subtlety.

As orange juice and strong Turkish coffee are brought to Slobo on a silver tray, quite other pleasures are unfolding in the Bosnian village of Mali Voćnjak. The village boys are celebrating the arrival of a military treasure: a rumbling, clanking, diesel-spewing, battle-scarred Yugoslav National Army tank, twenty-five kilometres *inside* the new state of Bosnia-Hercegovina. Slobo will not abandon his Serb brothers, now imprisoned on their own land by the Western-backed Islamic Conspiracy. I observe the spectacle with my long-time friend and neighbour, Mihajlo. We sit, Mika and I, in our custom of many years, on two old chairs next to the woodpile beside his house. Here one can catch the sun for almost the whole day, can turn east and look to the wooded hills rising to Žrtvova Mountain, or south and west to the village streets and houses sloping to the Jadar River, whose name means sorrow. Today, the peace of the river was tainted by an approaching whine and grumble, then the appearance of a mottled war machine from around a bend. Now we watch as the tank growls and lurches up the hill from the river road, spinning its treads and flinging spring mud at young fools who venture too near. Boys laugh at their bespattered pals, then crow in stunned delight as they are plastered themselves. Mothers' shouts are ignored, barely heard.

The thrill! To be in the presence of such brute, seasoned power! They drink in the fumes and savour in their guts the animal roar of the engine, the clank of steel chucked against steel as the treads race round, slewing through the brick-red muck and biting into tree roots for purchase. The armour plate is pocked and rusted, paint shot away. Grease is black on the wheel hubs, smeared thick on the telescoping barrel of the turret gun.

A few boys launch themselves at the fenders and clamber aboard, wrap arms round the greasy barrel or straddle it and punch fists into the air. Some cling to the fenders inches above the advancing track. One track finds a buried boulder while the other spins, and the beast lurches and shimmies, metal screaming against rock. A boy falls. One leg enters the space between wheels and tread and he is spun once around like a doll and thrown free, his screams lost in the din. The tank grinds on and the boy lies in the weeds of the ditch, one leg from the knee down a mash of blood and bone, and some boys now gather round to stare as if hypnotized by the screams and the flesh that is something from the butcher's. An older boy tears off his shirt and fashions a tourniquet, and in the weeks ahead the maimed boy's mother sees that she must thank God. Her son is useless as a soldier.

This tank and others following and the sweaty brandy-soaked young bulls inside come triumphant from Zvornik. They are all Serbs but not all from Serbia. Bosnian peasants and Yugo soldier-boys have joined to avenge real and mythic Turkish crimes. Their victory: Zvornik secured and pillaged, raped, thousands killed, some of them thrown beneath the treads of tanks. Even children. This was witnessed. And tens of thousands driven from the town, driven from bedrooms and kitchens and mosques if not murdered there. All of them Muslim but for a few mixed-marriage Serbs and a handful of Croats.

A handful. This phrase issued from a German journalist, a grave young man who lingered yesterday morning at our hospital, questioning, gazing steadily, pausing to change the tapes in his machine. He spoke our language, putting polite corners on it. He was intrigued by my roommate Ernad, a Muslim born in Zvornik. The German had read books from America, the early exposés of "ethnic cleansing." From his confident storehouse of knowledge he imparted to Ernad the stale news from Zvornik: estimates of deaths, rapes, refugees. Then the tossed-off phrase, *and perhaps a handful of Croats.* So, the news of Bosnia, from New York via Munich to Sarajevo.

Scribbling foreigners, an assessing army: our blessing and our curse. Let us observe one now in progress on a tome. Her subject is inhumanity. She is bent over a desk in a book-lined study in Boston or Chicago or some university town, her mouth twisted, chewing a tag of skin inside her cheek, getting closer to ...

She sifts through sheaves of notes. She is one hundred pages into her opus, its meanings always in her mind. She opens a text crammed with pencilled notes, an early report from the Balkan upheaval. Flipping pages. Here: "Zvornik ... JNA units ... the stair-wells choked with bodies ... streets washed with blood ... 42,000 driven out ... no more than handful of Croats." She stares at the page. Not five hundred. Not one hundred. A handful. Hardly worth mentioning. The writer's mind stutters. She wishes to be neutral. The slate waiting for the message. She writes to create or discover a message. Something true. A good truth, perhaps a helpful one. She sits in a darkening room with her face turned to grey light from the window. Bare tree branches. Winter sky. Her mind is stumbling, staggers forward, can go no further. She's on the edge of something. She's on the lip of a cliff and knows she must not look down. Better her brain be cordoned or shut off than that it begin reeling, careening out of its reasoned orbit. Her mouth is dry, and this is what takes her out of her chair to the kitchen tap, where she is surprised by a group of soldiers who burst in and rape her there on the floor, the last one slitting her throat as he achieves orgasm. This is what her mind constructs, an incident she has read about, but as if happening now in her own kitchen, in her mind's eye, as she runs cool water into a clean glass. And the Zvornik tanks. The children. The water is a balm on her tightening throat.

She doesn't go back to her computer. She goes from room to room turning on lights. She can hear the television. Her daughter is watching *The Simpsons*. When she enters the room she sees Homer Simpson with his head caught absurdly in the gears of a carnival ride. As her daughter laughs uncontrollably at Homer's plight she stares at the screen and feels that she understands nothing, and never will. Later in bed she will think of her great grandparents, Croats who were killed in Yugoslavia in 1943. She has a sepia photograph from their wedding. She knows how they died. She knows this is why she's writing the book. To tease a meaning from all the deaths. Right now the point eludes her. The point of writing anything at all. Because men do these things. Conceive and do them. Shoot helpless old folks. Crush living children. Her husband is breathing beside her. She gets out of bed and stands at the window. Snow is falling. It sifts gently down through circles of streetlight.

Within hours of the Serb militia's arrival in Mali Voćnjak, most of our few dozen Muslim families had fled to the old Muslim village of Gavranica, a ten-minute drive east along the river road. A few chose more remote ground, climbing the twisting dirt track that rose through oak and pine forest to the mountain hamlet of Brzačići. The Serbs of our village were left either to celebrate the purge or secretly lament the loss of friends. To openly regret the loss of a Muslim neighbour was to show a naive or reckless sentiment. To call his "cleansing" a barbarity was near-treasonous. It was now more honourable to break into his house, trample his family photos and steal his television. Mika wondered aloud if I should leave and I was adamant: no goon squad would force me from my home of thirty years.

"Go," he said. "Go to your daughter's in Medvedja. No one can be trusted now. You'll be betrayed by someone who covets your house. The Chetniks will demand your papers and then what? Half-Serb is not enough for these idiots."

I would hear none of it. Give away my house to back-stabbers and marauding criminals? They had already stolen my little Fića and crashed it into the river. And Zlata had her own troubles. And I would not leave the house in which I was properly to die at a ripe old age. Fuck them! They could go back to their mothers' pussies! I would stay and be an honourable Serb.

Mika pushed out his lips. He shook his head. I was red and puffing, my jaw set. Later we got drunk. We drank to freedom, hearing the soldier drunks bellowing and wasting bullets in the night. Two headstrong old pals, whose affections were pared to the certainty of one inviolable friendship, who lived in the houses they had built when roads were dirt trails and there was not a TV antenna to be seen, when everyone walked everywhere, or, if need be, took a horse cart. The village had one automobile when I built my house. Only two tractors. And these tractors were borrowed and shared all round. I was barely thirty and Hana twenty-four, with a baby on the way, Marko. Then Zlata. Now they were lost or gone from me, and my house and my memory and Mika were my only companions. So now was I simply to up and leave? To run from impudent snarling pups who should go back to Serbia where their mothers could scold them and wash their dirty behinds because they hadn't the sense to do it themselves? To be forced out by these swaggering pansy boys? What a thought! There was nothing but to stay. To live my life such as it lasted in my own village.

Mika and I had become fathers and old men together. We had drunk late each weekend and endured our wives' complaints, while Hana and Ćamila too would ignore us to drink coffee and gabble for whole afternoons like devoted sisters. We all watched out for one another, shared food and possessions and the care of our animals. Then we lost Marko, and Hana's descent began, and within four years she too was gone. Not a month after her funeral, Mika arrived early one morning, already drunk, to say that Ćamila had gone for good to her sister in Bijeljina. Though we could hardly express it, we knew that we were bound more tightly. We sat nights in long silences or sharing words of little meaning but vital comfort, and we learned to laugh again, and to dispute again on the nature of the world and of men and women. And as we did this, we watched the ghosts of old terrors begin to rise again from the Yugoslav earth.

The commander of the Serb "liberators" of Mali Voćnjak came to my house with Simo Kraljević, a local scowler, the sort of man who feels he is always at a calculated disadvantage in all human affairs, who will drive sourly past a neighbour trudging hatless in the rain or feed poisoned meat to any dog that dares to piss on his roses. About 1980 I had sold Simo a cow, and within a week the cow became lame from tumbling down into a stream bed because Simo had no fence along the bank. Then the injured cow, treated ineptly by Simo himself, developed an infection that killed it, and so I was ever after the man who had purposely sold him a clumsy and sickly cow. Now, some ten years on, here was Simo come to steal my house (just as Mika said), made brave by the hulking Chetnik who would demand my papers and confirm the charge that I was a scheming Turk.

From his window, Mika saw them on my doorstep. He took a bottle of his best brandy and came over to defend me. In my kitchen stood the Chetnik and Simo, the former staring at my birth and marriage documents which proved the women in my life to have been my own blood enemies. Then from the yard came Mika's voice shouting, "Saint Vasilije! Miracle worker! Praise the day!" He was somewhat wrong about the date, but our Chetnik was oblivious. Thus Mika stuck his neck out for me. Playing a state of happy though not sloppy drunkenness, he entered my house, lauding the saint who had saved him from boyhood death at the hands of the Ustashas. All an inspired lie, a manipulation of Christian zeal and Serbian myth, all for the benefit of the glowering bearded one who'd come to scan my bookshelves for the Koran.

Simo stared at the performance with disgust; the Chetnik, with dull suspicion. Simo (pious Simo!) said Mika was a week off on his Saint's Day, and they argued ludicrously, Mika insisting he was only a day off, and what difference did it make when he owed his life to the miracle that occurred fifty years ago this very day? Mika turned as if seeing the Chetnik for the first time: "Slobo! You have an honoured guest!"

He raised his hand in salute, then took glasses from my shelf. He poured brandy for four and we drank to Serbia. Then another round for St. Vasilije of Ostrog. No one could refuse, though Simo's face was like a thundercloud. Mika's eyes glistened. He crossed himself and gazed up through my roof as if toward the saintly abode. Then we drank to the other Slobo, and to Radovan, and to fearsome Arkan, and finally to our present Chetnik, Mika bowing deeply from the waist. Then abruptly he was gone, calling over his shoulder that he was going to the church to pray. A superb performance, which I rounded off by apologizing for the intrusion. It was a yearly event, I said, my own eyes glistening with the depth of our comradeship.

I had to face more questions from the Chetnik. He was no easy mark. Pondering my documents, he demanded more brandy, which I freely gave. He downed it and said, "Where is your wife?"

"She is in heaven. Gone three years."

Two more questions forced lies from me, lies about my Hana to save my own skin.

"Where is she buried?"

"The Orthodox cemetery in Medvedja, Serbia," I said.

He frowned; he had likely never heard of Medvedja. "She was converted?"

I shrugged as if astounded. "Of course, how else could we marry? How else to raise my children?"

Simo sputtered, red-faced: "He's lying. She went to her people in Sarajevo, and to the mosque in Gavranica, all the time."

I gave a sad laugh, shook my head: "Such unquenchable grief, Simo, for a cow ten years dead, and by your own careless hand."

Simo exploded, "Your cow was half-dead when I bought her!"

The Chetnik downed a last glassful: "Why don't you shoot each other then, hey?" He stood and clumped out, followed by Simo, who turned at the door and urged me to insert my dead cow into my mother's Turkish pussy.

The days went by and more militiamen arrived, filling the empty Muslim houses. They built bonfires and roasted the sheep and goats left behind. They chose a few dwellings for target practice, blasting them with tank guns and even mortar shells. They dispatched stray dogs with rocket-powered grenades. When every structure they deemed extraneous was beyond further degradation they began shooting the tops off trees on the slopes behind the town, as if consummate ruin was their notion of paradise. I began to feel that I could slit every one of their throats without a shred of remorse.

Then things abruptly became properly military. JNA officers arrived and sobered the tinctured garrison with steely authority. The Chetnik commander was reduced to surly acquiescence. Trucks entered from the Zvornik road hauling mortars and artillery. The occupying militia were trained on the guns and sent with them high into the mountains east of the village, where they dug in and began to rain shells upon the Muslim stronghold of Srebrenica. One day they turned their guns a few degrees to the north and with a few hours of idle fire laid waste to Brzačići, scattering or murdering our few villagers who had lugged their belongings up the mountainside in hopes of a refuge safer than nearby Gavranica. But within a month, a new wave of Serbs swept through Gavranica as well. People were burned in their houses. The mosque was dynamited. Men were trucked to a remote gorge and executed, their bodies thrown into deep crevasses (pits already glutted with memory: the bones of Serbs killed by Ustashas and their Muslim allies). Women were taken to a school gymnasium, where they were held for days and raped. Released, they moved along the roads like walking dead. This action set the stage for the arrival in September of avenging Muslim militias. As Mika and I hid in his cellar, the Serbs were driven from Mali Voćnjak in a three-day battle that left the town all but empty of civilian life, a ghost town scattered with dead and peopled by victorious thugs and a handful of benumbed old people.

Within a few days, Mika had been casually murdered, and I was a bloodied figure standing amid the charred rubble of my house. There a foreign TV crew found me, and quickly judged my identity too confusing to be newsworthy.

Chapter Twenty-seven

Srebrenica was perhaps four hours by car from Strastanica, via a winding route that hugged the Drina, skirted Višegrad, then veered from the river and made its way through deep gorges and mountain passes to Žepa and beyond — the same landscape that Slobodan Kušić had traversed as a child. As for Zvornik, Stefan could not hear mention of the town without his face going dark. The twins' parents had been killed that April, during the first massive Serb offensive across the Drina. Lately Stefan had begun speaking again of his niece, the twins' sister. Separated from her brothers during the Zvornik attack, she'd been living with family friends in a secure Serb hamlet near Borika. Cousins of Stefan's in Belgrade had agreed to take the child, but the question of how to get her out remained.

Zvornik had been briefly prominent in the news before I'd left Toronto. Axel would comment darkly on the coverage. He arrived from work one day with unedited tapes of the Vukovar devastation. The images were shocking, but they were old news from the Croatian war. They had nothing to do with Sandjak or Strastanica. At one point Axel said, "And you want to go and live among these people?" then he quickly retracted it, acknowledging his regression to mindless slur — as if my monks had been firing the JNA mortars on the TV screen.

As Axel unwound in the bars after dinner, I stood in Toni's apartment eyeing the cassettes he'd brought to New York; they sat before me on Toni's VCR. I'd been avoiding them. Whatever they contained, whatever selective news of Bosnian atrocity, it would not reflect the world I knew. I would see the images through the lens Slobo had given me. And through Stefan's lens, though his was still veiled. I had already reshaped Slobo's images into my own story of Stefan's history — and of Pimm's.

Toni was in bed. I poured myself a Scotch and scanned the labels on Axel's cassettes. I went and ensured that Toni's bedroom door was closed, then I put the tape marked *Zvornik/Tuzla* into the machine.

There is no talking head, no voice-over — it's raw, unedited footage. A road lined with blasted apartment blocks. Beyond them, tile-roofed stucco houses shot full of holes, burned. Tanks parked in the street, wrecked cars. Distant cracks of gunfire. The camera is on the move and nervous, oddly close to the ground, at hip level or lower, searching jerkily, panning across the road to a river gorge, a steel-beam bridge. Sometimes the lens is briefly obscured, then uncovered again. An armoured vehicle is rumbling across the steel bridge. Its big tires run over a human corpse. There are other bodies on the bridge. The camera shifts to the river, a floating body sliding quickly away in the sluice between rocky banks toward a landscape of spring green. An explosion and the image swings wildly, a blur of motion and flashes of streetscape, then long seconds of black ending in a steadying gaze at an apartment block, zooming in on a balcony veiled with smoke, masonry crumbling, then a pan down to a tank in the street that fires again, the sound of the hit, and the pan up to another plume of smoke and billowing dust. The tank continues a desultory barrage while the lens stays fixed on the disintegrating balcony.

Cut to a concrete stairwell, bright with blood and choked with mangled bodies. Light and lens move in tandem over the slaughter. Everything is revealed in halogen clarity. Every gaping jaw, staring eye or socket, every blossoming wound, twisted limb, meaty bone, splayed gut, white tendon. The camera settles on a face. A half-face. A half-head. There is nothing above the nose. A flesh-and-bone brain pan, a ragged red bowl. The mouth is wide, teeth bared and flecked pink, two clotted trickles dribbling down a delicate chin and milky unblemished neck.

I sank onto the couch and put my head between my knees. Acid moved up from my gut. I groped for the remote and stopped the tape. The taste of bile. I swallowed it down. Some deep breaths. Waiting. Until I could stand and move to the kitchen for some water.

In the morning Axel was not in evidence. Probably he'd slept at Toshi's. Toni was at her desk. I asked if she'd viewed the tapes.

"Not for long."

"How long?"

"A few minutes. Martin was here yesterday. He asked if he could look at them. He was in Zvornik last year. I can't handle that stuff — print yes, but not on video. I left him to it. They're not broadcast tapes."

"I know."

"Martin said he'd seen worse. I couldn't figure that one out."

Toni later went out. I found myself on the couch, staring at my ghost in the TV's grey eye. I started the *Zvornik/Tuzla* cassette where I'd left off. An experiment — which proved again that I couldn't bear it. I pressed fast-forward while I shot glances at the screen, watching for something less ghastly. When the image cut to outdoors I pushed play.

A dirt road approaching a cluster of houses. Again the walking camera, not so furtive now. It finds a message sprayed across a shrapnel-pocked wall: NOVA SRPSKA. It pans across some fresh graves with slender white markers. Muslim dead. Cut to a horse and wagon on a village street. The cameraman approaching from behind, hurrying to catch up. There are two uniformed corpses in the wagon. Up front a young woman and an old man. The cameraman addresses the pair in rapid Serbo-Croat. The wagon stops and the old man says to the camera, "*Da, uzete slike.*" Take pictures, he says. He sweeps his hand round to the bodies: "My grandson and his friend." Their faces are covered with a blood-stained blanket. He lifts the blanket. The men's throats are slit.

The camera shifts to the woman, who stares straight ahead at the road, clutching herself. The man flicks the reins and the horse plods on. A woman comes out of a house and empties a bucket of water. She turns and stares bitterly at the camera.

Next is hospital footage, a man on a gurney in a corridor, his bloody trousers shredded, nurses hooking up an IV line. The nurses work in dull silence. In the shadows along the corridor are more gurneys, wheelchairs, people in them and under blankets on the floor. Next, a lean grey-haired man is moving among the wounded in their beds. He wears a crisp combat uniform, four stars on the epaulette, a U.N. badge pinned to his beret. He stops at each bed and asks a few questions. He glances at some beds and moves on, guessing that conversation will not succeed. He speaks precise French, a woman translating into Serbo-Croatian. One amputee's genitals are fully exposed, the camera taking them in for long seconds at the bottom of the frame before at last tilting up just enough to exclude them. The patients seem bewildered or indifferent, the general weary, bored even, but dutifully grave. Then he looks at the camera: "*C'est tout?*" The tape goes blank.

Chapter Twenty-eight

On the plane with Axel I realized I'd left his videos sitting on Toni's VCR. I said nothing. For two days I'd been stifling my turmoil over what I'd seen. Axel hadn't mentioned the tapes since he'd arrived in New York with them.

That night in his Toronto apartment, as he breezed in from walking Oscar, I confessed that I'd left the cassettes at Toni's. He barely glanced at me.

"Oh, it doesn't matter. They're copies."

He disappeared into the kitchen. I worked up a head of steam at his insouciance — as if this record of slaughter were a spare set of holiday snapshots. He began banging around in the kitchen, then called out testily: "Did you ever look at them?"

I didn't answer. He resumed slamming cupboards. When I finally spoke the pitch of my anger surprised me.

"Yes, I looked at them! At one. One was enough."

I could picture him poised over the sink, guilty-defiant. He came into the living room.

"I only wanted you to be aware of what can happen."

"I'm not aware?"

"Just so you'll think twice before —"

"Wait a minute. You think I'm not aware?"

He stopped, watching my face, and his newsroom savvy seemed to droop a little. He could see that he'd lit a fuse. We stood there with it fizzing. He changed tack.

"I know it's difficult stuff. If it upset you I'm sorry."

"Doesn't it upset you, Axel, watching that?"

"Well, you know, it's on the shelf. It's coming in all the time. Rwanda, Chechnya, East Timor —"

"Stop it. Stop rhyming off your knowledge. As if you know what my life is about."

He pulled a tight smile. A knowing and regretful smile for my pain, my naiveté.

"Chris, you're missing it completely. I just don't want you hurt. Toni said you want to go someplace near Goražde now —"

"No. No. You're missing it. You're missing everything that's happened to me. If I go or don't go to Bosnia it's got nothing to do with your tapes, with this obscenity you foisted on me. Just to prove you have some sway, some expertise that's supposed to knock sense into me, like I'm an idiot tourist just stumbling around looking for thrills. I know what's happening in Bosnia. I know it better than you."

"How? How can you know? You watch RTS in a bar."

"But that's exactly what you gave me, forced on me. Worse than RTS. How dare you assault me with this horrible stuff, insult me, manipulate me, as if my two years of life there is worth nothing, worth less than a few frames of war porn."

"It's not porn. It's real. It's data."

"Keep it! How could you think it would help me? Stefan is not data. The bodies are not data, and the funerals, mothers wailing in the church and the pictures of teenagers taped to coffins. It's my life. Stefan's sister and her husband were killed in Zvornik. Their boys live with us. We listen to their night terrors. The soldiers come back from Goražde and they have dinner with us, and I'm looking at this dead thing behind their eyes. They sit in Čeko's and brag about killing and they drink themselves comatose with the stuff they've seen and done. This is my life, Axel. You're only rubbing my nose in the gore. To prove to yourself — you can't prove it to me — that you're the wise one and I need you, I need to be protected. Well I don't, especially not by you. You spent ten days in Dubrovnik. You don't know any more about Bosnia than any TV viewer in Toronto. Does your stack of videos give you special knowledge?"

"Yes."

"Bullshit. Piles of corpses are not the truth about Bosnia."

"They are, and it'll only get worse. It's not my fantasy."

"Your fantasy is that you know the world because you have the power to aim a camera at it, because you can seek out people at their worst, victims, perpetrators, one shock after another. The six-o'clock horror show. It's obscene. It's pitiful."

"Chris, stop this."

"You know nothing about my life!"

I don't know what I said after that. Something broke loose. The memory is noise. My throat rasping, blood behind my eyes, Axel crunched up on the sofa, Oscar yapping in panic.

Axel had insisted that I confront the worst. Was I supposed to concede something to him? Well I wouldn't. In bed I flip-flopped between fury and guilty conscience. Next morning I apologized for the outburst, for losing my temper. Axel stared into his coffee.

"It wasn't like you. The violence."

Then he was out of his chair, briskly washing up, and out the door to work.

Toronto felt like an animated memory; every outing presented reminders of what I'd lost or consciously left behind. After two nights of Church Street dinners with old friends (hugs and kisses, manic chatter, and again those blank faces as I tried to describe my life), I retreated into dutiful phone calls. I hardly left Axel's apartment.

Pimm's ashes were in Mt. Pleasant Cemetery. Hoping for sun I delayed my visit, and on the day of my departure was presented with a cloudless china-blue sky. I rode the subway up to St. Clair. Fighting a frigid wind, I walked north to the cemetery gates. I followed the winding drive to Section M, crossed the pallid grass past familiar stones (LATIMER, THORPE, CRAIGLEE) and stood over the Hoekstra plot. Pimm's name was carved under his parents', Dirk and Erma. The stone was stark in the sunlight. An overgrown yew bush crowded it from behind. As usual, I was unmoved. I knew this about graves: they don't evoke their occupants. It still surprised me. I touched the black granite and found it warm. Then I realized I'd forgotten to stop at the florist's under Axel's building. I had planned to leave a red rose. But I could see it would only have looked abandoned on the muddy grass.

As I sat on the southbound train my mind leapt to Strastanica. The feathery pines and clean snow, drift of woodsmoke, the big fireplace crackling at supper time in the dining room; Stefan's eyes throwing unreadable code at me across the table, or simply refusing to meet my gaze at all. He was infuriating. And he was deeply vulnerable. As the train rattled toward Bloor Street I whispered to Pimm, *He's not you*. But I couldn't wait to get on the plane.

Chapter Twenty-nine

I was one of about twenty people on the afternoon flight from Zagreb. We touched down in Dubrovnik at dusk. Rain swept across the tarmac, but the air when we emerged was almost balmy. Sea spray fanned in under the streetlights as my taxi turned onto Frana Supila. Hauling my luggage across the deserted lobby of the Lastovo I noted the doorman lounging at the bar. I ventured an *izvinite* and left the bags for him.

The desk clerk checked me in, then said the manager would like a word. In a windowless office fogged with cigarette smoke I was told that my car had been stolen from the hotel garage. Was I aware that the hotel recommended removal of the battery and distributor rotor if vehicles were stored unused? I said I'd not been informed of this. He said it was standard advice to all guests, as long as the war economy was playing into the hands of criminals. He slid a police report across the desk, dialled the station for me and handed me the receiver. A secretary put me through to a sullen cop who took down the number for Strastanica. I knew I'd never hear from them. I felt like kicking myself, and the cops, and the hotel management.

Upstairs, I called Toni in New York and left a message. I knew her Land Rover was sitting idle in Podgorica. I splashed my face with water, poured some brandy and sat down to watch the news, flipping between Croatian reports and ghostly, flickering images from the independent Bosnian channel. Both reported that Serbs were firing anti-tank missiles into Sarajevo's downtown. There were images of blasted apartment buildings, cars speeding along Sniper Alley, people sprinting across streets to the crack of rifle fire; then a pan across the hills, smoke and flash blooming out of gun emplacements, the crumps of firing and detonation. Both channels said fifty-odd U.N. peacekeeper hostages had been released by Bosnian Serbs. I knew there were Canadians among the recent U.N. hostages, but my sympathies were more with the people they were sent to protect — and mostly with Slobo, in Kostreša Hospital.

After dinner I tried Toni again and she picked up on the first ring. Of course I could have the Rover. She'd need it back mid-January, but perhaps that could be my excuse to finally get away to Kotor.

In the morning I went to Dubrovačka Banka and, using a credit card, came away with 10,000 Deutschmarks. I had to wait an hour while the clerk arranged to have cash transferred crosstown from Gruž. I hoped it was enough to buy me a decent vehicle on the black market. Toni's Rover would be mine for barely a month.

I caught the noon bus to Podgorica. At the border into Montenegro the guards pulled every bag from the cargo bay and casually poked through them on the wet pavement. They let me keep the coffee and herbal tea I'd bought in New York, but confiscated my bottle of Zagreb brandy. They didn't ask how much cash I had. Two German backpackers were led toward the customs building and we entered Yugoslavia without them. By three I was in a taxi heading for Antonia's apartment. She'd phoned ahead to a neighbour who had charge of the Rover's keys. The woman was a widow, her apartment so chill and spotless and bare of ornament, and she so pinched and melancholy, that it was all I could do to stay a few moments and accept a coffee.

The Rover was in a fenced and guarded lot. The tank was empty, probably siphoned by the guard. The windshield wipers and spare jerry cans were inside Toni's apartment. By the time I got myself roadworthy and was on the motorway to Sandjak the daylight was gone. The twisting blacktop led through deep cuts of rock and black tunnels, and by nine I was growling up the grade to Strastanica in a fog of swirling flakes. Snow was banked waist-high; Petko had been out with the tractor. I parked and went in through the kitchen, and found Father Nikolaj over a whistling kettle. For a frozen moment he stared like I was a stranger.

"Chris. God help you. You look like Croat. Where is beard?"

"Growing."

He stuck out his hand and I bent and grazed it with my lips.

"I brought coffee and tea, Father."

I hefted a bag onto the table and dug out the goods. Scanning the packages, Nikolaj mentioned that I'd missed a choir rehearsal.

"I'm sorry, Father. My car was stolen."

"You walk from Dubrovnik? Is good excuse."

I left him sniffing a box of Cranberry Camomile, his shrubby brows striving for an opinion.

I stuck my head into the dining hall. Dositej and Filaret were listening to the news. They stood and welcomed me, dip-bowing with quick smiles. I returned their *God help*, left my bags in the vestibule, and went straight to Stefan's room. I knocked and the door opened almost at once. We took in each other's faces, and to me he seemed a little older, more weary. We embraced and he stepped away. With a hint of smile he said in Serbian, "You're late."

"My car was stolen. I had to borrow Toni's Rover."

"We prayed for your safety. You might have telephoned."

"It was difficult getting away at all."

"Perhaps."

"Not perhaps. It simply was."

"All right."

He looked at me, in his glance that flash that always seemed to temper affection with a subtle dig. He took a page of music from the bedside table and held it out to me.

"Something new. I think it's time."

I looked at the music — a baritone clef, a single line of notes unspooling. A solo, three pages worth, handwritten.

"You wrote this?"

"I copied it at Hilandar. Take it. We'll begin tomorrow. We must work hard to prepare you."

"Stefan, I'm delighted."

"You had a good visit to Toronto?"

"Very good."

"I'm pleased. And you must be tired. So, time for bed. Welcome home."

Another hug, a brotherly kiss, then he was holding the door for me.

Chapter Thirty

Two weeks before Christmas a fax message was slid under my door.

Poštovani oče Nikolaje:

Molim Vas prosledite ovaj faks Christopher Maitland što pre.

Chris,

I'm leaving NY tonight. My sister's in hosp. in Podgorica with stroke. They say she'll live. Mater is en-route from Trieste. Maybe you can drive down at some point. It would be nice to see you, and I'll need the Rover. I can get by for a day or two if you're delayed.

Toni

I told Stefan the news. He suggested I take the solo music with me, though I'd already memorized it.

On a cloudless winter morning, I made my way south through the Tara canyon. The river was a blue ribbon winding through pristine snow. The suburbs of Podgorica brought me back to earth.

Mrs. Perović answered the door to Toni's apartment. She seemed glad to have someone to coddle, moved about making coffee and warming some pastries she'd made. With a sad smile she watched me eat. Toni was with Jelena. She was due back shortly and Mater would return with her to the hospital. I was free to join them if I didn't have other business.

I'd not known Jelena well; I thought I'd only be an added burden at the hospital. And I did have other business. I needed to buy a car.

Toni arrived, relieved to see me. We drove to the hospital and it was agreed I would return at supper hour. I went on a hunt through the diesel-fogged streets for a respectable black-market vehicle. If I could find one, it would likely relieve me of most of the cash Velcroed inside my pants. I knew where to start: the outdoor central market. I wandered into the frigid labyrinth of stalls and asked a babushka where I might find auto accessories. A few minutes later I was talking to a large unshaven man over a table loaded with used tools and car radios. His mug of tea steamed with the whiff of brandy. I told him I needed a good 4x4. He called to a friend.

We drove to the outskirts of town, to a factory building on a large lot enclosed by barbed wire fencing. A man opened the gate to admit us. The lot was filled with wrecked and cannibalized vehicles and in a separate section refurbished ones, washed and gleaming in tidy rows on the thawing mud. There were two 4x4s, both oil-burners under the spit and polish. After a little haggling, I sacrificed most of my stash for another Golf, thinking that I might at least have found my own among those on offer — but it would have been galling to have to pay twice for it. My new wheels followed me back to Toni's.

I drove the salesman back to his market stall and took a few minutes to check out a table selling audio tapes. The monastery had a modest collection of religious and folk music, played on a tape deck that Petko had rigged to the dining room hi-fi. At weddings Nikolaj even allowed pop tunes to enter the mix. Flipping through rip-offs of U2 and Madonna and Serb turbo-folk, I shifted for someone carting a box of videos and heard a greeting. I looked up at a face I knew. The videos and the red parka brought it home, but his name wouldn't come. He grinned at me.

"Chris! How goes it?"

"Fine!"

He continued on into a tent at the back of the stall, calling over his shoulder.

"I am Hariz!"

"Yes, yes, Hariz. How are you?"

He emerged.

"I am okay! You want tape?"

"Um ... Do you have a religious section?"

"No. Religious? No. Come inside. We have video. Come!"

He ducked through the tent flap. As I followed behind him, the grandpa minding the tape table winked and gave me a gummy grin. Inside were shelves filled with videos. The sleeves offered glossy close-ups of breasts and buttocks, spreading labia, puckered holes, hard cocks. Hariz unloaded more cassettes onto a shelf.

"What you doing in Podgorica?"

"I have a friend here."

"Girlfriend?"

"Well, yes."

"Name?"

"Antonia."

"She is pretty?"

"We're just friends."

"You must fix."

"No, no, nothing to fix."

"Okay. You like that one?"

My fingers had grazed a cassette. The cover photo showed an unbelievably huge penis nuzzling up to a rosebud anus. Pink lettering shouted the title, GUZPODAR, a pun meaning, roughly, "butt-master."

"Cheap for you. Ten Deutschmark."

"I don't have a VCR."

"Must phone Mujo. You loose number?"

"Mujo?"

"I phone for you."

"No, it's okay."

"You like this?" He took the cassette from the shelf.

"I can't play it, Hariz."

"Mujo can get for you."

"I don't want."

"Not VCR. He get you some good time. What you are wanting?" Hariz gazed openly at me, awaiting my answer. Suddenly I was considering the prospect of what he might "get" for me.

"A woman?"

"No. But thank you."

He placed the tape back on the rack.

"Okay. Not woman. What?"

"Nothing."

He broke into a crooked smile. With a little laugh he glanced away, then looked back at me, serious, watching my face.

"I must finish here. You come again six."

"I'm having dinner with someone."

"Girlfriend?"

"She's a friend, Hariz."

"What time you are free tonight?"

"Maybe nine, ten?"

"Is okay. Come to Špilja Bar. You know?"

"No."

He told me where to find Špilja Bar.

I met Toni and her mother at the hospital. Toni's first words were, "I'm starved, let's go to Mitar." She drove us to Ul. Slobode. In the restaurant her mother signalled to the waiter before we'd even sat down. She wanted a wine list. Toni levelled a firm gaze at her. Mater's doctors did not allow wine, but Toni didn't press the point. A bottle of Vranac was ordered.

They spoke Italian, including me with snatches of Serb and English. Jelena was regaining some mobility, but could not put a sentence together. The doctors blamed sanctions. The Nikšić hospital had been short of drugs and staff. Jelena was rushed to Podgorica, nearly an hour away. They'd been powerless to halt the brain damage in its early stages. "It's probably true," said Toni. "Fucking war." Her mother's face twitched, a flash of admonition, then she put down her knife and fork and touched her napkin to brimming eyes. There was nothing more to say.

We drove back to Toni's building and I pointed out my rein-carnated Golf in the lot, then I bade them goodnight. Toni gave me a significant look and handed me her key: "I'll make the couch up for you."

Špilja Bar was next to a grocery on a street of low-rise apartment blocks. It was boisterous with young guys shooting pool and knocking back Nikšić beer. Hariz didn't show up. About midnight I went back to Toni's, willed my mind clear of speculation, and slept.

Chapter Thirty-one

Hariz was at his market booth next morning, smiling.

"Chris! You get lost?"

"I was there, Hariz. Before nine."

"How long you are waiting?"

"Till twelve."

"I am coming twelve!"

"You were coming, or you were there?"

"I was coming there!"

"All right, you were late."

"Yes! Okay Chris — you are busy now?"

"I'm utterly available."

"*Šta?*"

"*Nisam zauzet.*"

"Okay! We go for the coffee."

He said a few words to the sweater-bundled grandpa and we went out to the street.

"You have car?"

I pointed out my car.

"Is new colour."

"New car. The other was stolen."

"Ha! This also is stolen. Big chance."

"I hope not, I just registered it."

"Maybe police visit you someday, when they are not too busy."

I suppressed that thought and got behind the wheel. Hariz climbed in beside me.

"Where are we going, Hariz?"

He bugged his eyes at me.

"Crazy. You want to go?"

"Where did you hear that one?"

"You know?"

"It's old as the hills."

"I think in Dubrovnik, before war. Tourista job."

I started the car and pulled into the street: "We could go to my friend's apartment. If you like."

"Girlfriend."

"Yes."

"She is there?"

"No. Gone for the day."

"Okay. We go."

I had to knock at Mrs. Janković's for the spare key. She stood in her doorway and watched me go into the apartment with Hariz. I hung our coats and told him to make himself at home, I'd make some coffee. He sat on the edge of the couch, glancing around at the bookshelves. I set the coffee to boil and rejoined him.

"Your friend is reading very much."

"She's a teacher. History. She could tell you the whole history of Sandjak."

"But I know this."

"I'm sure you do."

He sat back on the couch. Then he abruptly leaned forward and pulled off his sweater.

"Is hot inside here."

He glanced at me, his cheeks flushed. I went and dealt with the coffee. When I brought it in he was lying full length on the couch, his face turned to the cushions. He had one arm flung back over his head, revealing two inches of flat stomach between T-shirt and belt. Inside his jeans, bent in an arc by the constriction, his penis pushed against the denim. Setting the coffee tray aside, I sat on the couch beside his knees. He shifted and stretched as if half asleep. Eyes closed, face still turned half away, he reached down and adjusted his jeans, unkinking his bent cock. It became a thick ridge that paralleled his fly and ran up to his belt buckle, which I gently unclasped.

It was like sex at scout camp. I'd barely touched him, had only just got my hand round his pole, noting the clear bead glistening at its tip, when his mouth opened and his diaphragm pulsed up, forcing the hot breath from him, and I was wrestling his T-shirt up with one hand while the other tightly clutched his pumping cock, and coils of semen shot in a blur, arcing over him onto Toni's upholstery, her end table and a bowl of cellophaned mints. Then the flow quickly ebbed, laying a pearly string across Hariz's bunched T-shirt and ginger-fuzzed chest.

He glanced down at the mess as if he'd spilled ice cream on a Sunday shirt. I told him to stay put, went to the bathroom and returned with a warm washcloth and a towel. We tidied up, and I looked at him and said thank you. He released his quick scoffing laugh. There was no hope of a return on the favour. He briefly considered the damp spots on his T-shirt, then pulled his sweater over it. I poked through Mater's crystal mints, wiping and drying the sticky ones. He cupped his palm round the coffee pot.

"Is still hot."

"Why don't you pour us some?"

He tipped coffee into Toni's demitasses. Sipping from cup and saucer he stood at a bookshelf scanning titles, then moved on to her small selection of films on video.

"Your girlfriend is Italian?"

"And Yugoslav."

"She is not having Yugoslav movies. Ah, something is here: *Zvornik Tuzla*. I think is not movie."

"Let me see that."

He handed me the cassette. I stared at Axel's hasty lettering on the label. It was following me round the globe.

"Is news tape?"

"Yes."

"American?"

"Um, Canadian."

"Can we watch?"

"Maybe later."

"Is possible now?"

"Why?"

"I am ... what is word? *Radoznao.*"

"You're curious, yes. But it's old news, two years old."

"Attack of Zvornik."

"Yes. It's a terrible tape, Hariz."

"*Naravno* — Serbs are murdering Zvornik Muslims."

"Why do you want to see that?"

"Chris, you know why. Belgrade news is propaganda. You not want me to see real news?"

"It's not the whole story."

"Pa! You believe Slobo shit?"

"Of course not. He's a pig, a criminal."

"Pig is better. Pig you can eat."

I couldn't deny him the images. I was only painting myself a Serb sympathizer. I put the tape into Toni's machine.

The nervous camera, the street lined with tanks and wrecked apartment blocks, the sound of the rushing river and distant gunfire. Then the rusty steel-girder bridge, the scattered corpses. Hariz sat on the couch, eyes riveted to the screen.

"This is Drina Bridge at Zvornik."

"You know it?"

"Of course."

On the screen tank shells were ripping into the high-rise balcony. I knew the stairwell footage was next. I retreated to the kitchen. Soon I heard Hariz swearing, quiet oaths of shock, then a strangled sound that rose from his gut, then the swearing building to a black stream.

"Chris, come! You see!"

I stood in the kitchen doorway.

"Muslim. Only the Muslim people. Come!"

I approached the screen. He had paused the tape. He pointed at the juddering image, at a woman's twisted legs, then another's. "*Dimije*," he said. The two were wearing Muslim women's bloomers. Hariz fiddled with the remote, ran the image backward, forward, paused, until it came clear. He placed his finger on a young woman's bloody torso.

"Here." His voice was hoarse. "*Mjesec.*"

The girl wore a necklace. Resting in the hollow of her collarbone was a silver crescent moon. The shape shimmered and diffused as

I leaned closer. Hariz stared into my face. I could feel his breath.

"Not Serbs. No dead Serbs in Zvornik."

He restarted the tape. I couldn't stay with him. I went back to the kitchen. Hariz's stream of invective was exchanged for isolated bursts of fury; finally a long silence. Then I heard him in the entranceway. When I came into the hall, the apartment door was hanging open. I went out to the landing and caught the red flash of his parka, two floors down. A moment later I discovered he'd taken the tape.

That night I told Toni the story, leaving out the sex, which she'd likely surmised anyway. She had brought the tape for Martin Ivry. He'd wanted a copy but had to leave New York before he'd got it. Toni shrugged at my suggestion that it was now joining the video war. The tape was almost certainly in circulation already; a CBC correspondent had scrounged or stumbled on a copy in Bosnia and had brought it home. Martin might find it in Sarajevo if he dug a little. I pictured Derek Andover screening it over and over in his dark room at the Holiday Inn.

Jelena's daughter was due in from Belgrade. I had to vacate. Next morning I sat a long time in the car outside Toni's building, then I drove back to the market stall. Hariz wasn't there, but the old man said he'd left something for me. It was an unlabelled cassette. I went back to the apartment and stuck it into Toni's machine. For a few seconds the screen showed only a table and chair in a kitchen, then a figure moved into view. Hariz sat down and addressed the camera.

"Chris, I'm apologize for yesterday. I don't know why you are having this Zvornik and Tuzla video, who is giving, who gives this, to your friend. I take it because is important video. I say this also to your friend. On other part of this tape I'm making copy. So you have, and I have, because truth of Zvornik is hard to find in Serbia. In Bosna also."

He paused. "So Chris ... you still are the friend, I'm hoping. I think you have understanding that Serbs are bad peoples of this war. Most bad. This is truth. Many Serbs must pay, and Croats too, for what they do on Muslims. Maybe some they know this, and ask God to forgive. We must need, all peoples in this war, the forgiving." He shifted in his chair, looked away, then at the lens again. "Okay. *Dovidjenja*, Chris. I ask please you erase this part of tape. I think I see you again sometime. Maybe. You know where to find me."

He approached the camera and the image died, and a moment later the Zvornik pictures began.

Chapter Thirty-two

Our turnout for the Christmas service, concert and dinner was down somewhat due to heavy snow. Leftovers were sent home with the ones who'd braved the storm. My solo piece went without a hitch. There were prayers for peace, tributes to the dead. When all the guests had left or retired to their rooms I sat before a crackling fire in the dining hall with Stefan and Demitrios, Artemije, Luka and Barnabas, and we polished off most of a bottle of Strastanica brandy. We raised a familiar toast to Brotherhood in Christ. The second toast was from hulking greybeard Barnabas, who's like an ageing steely-eyed battle hero with hands like a carved Bogomil warrior's and a nose like a broadaxe. Always ready with a moral prod, he lifted his glass and caught my eye.

"To Chris, who sings like a believer."

They all drank, knowingly. Stefan had a wistful smile, staring into the fire. When the brandy had settled, Barnabas threw me another glance, refilling glasses.

"Perhaps you will succumb this year. Did God sing with you today?"

I had no answer. I'd sung intently, focused on getting every note perfect. Of course, the service had inspired me. But the stubborn working of intellect brought me always to the same impasse. What does it matter what we call it? The glimpse of peace. Of encompassing goodness. At that point, with Axel's video still fresh, in my head, I was even less inclined to label the mystery "God" or "Christ." As these things flashed through my mind and my response failed to come, I felt the blood rise into my face like I was a guilty schoolboy. Barnabas can do that to me. The brothers gazed thoughtfully at my flaming ears. Then Demitrios saved me, raising his glass to Sava, our own saint. In just three weeks there would be another party, his *Slava* day.

February brought more snow. I did my round of barn work, slogging silage in for cows and goats and sheep, slogging out manure. Then I was assigned a brand new obedience: I would assist in the slaughter. I led a sheep out to the hard-packed snow by the barn, where Brother Gerasim deftly flipped it onto its side. While I sat on the struggling creature he roped its legs immobile. With a powerful thrust and twisting of his wrist he slit the woolly throat and a crimson gush spurted steaming over the snow. We watched life ebb from the twitching body. It was all over in minutes. The sheep's plaintive bleats had peaked and stopped the instant the knife entered, and it bled in silence. I'd been apprehensive, but in the moment itself I was fully absorbed. It was the gutting and skinning that brought the beginnings of nausea, but I was simply too busy to let it take hold.

The animal became meat, the scent of blood like walking into a butcher shop and looking forward to dinner. As we worked on the big slab table in the kitchen pantry, blood to our elbows, Gerasim cupped the meaty rump in his hands and spoke of the mutton roast we'd have that night, and stew, and new pairs of gloves. When the body was a glistening carcass, all flesh and bone and silvery sinew, we hefted it into the kitchen and Brother Irinej set to work with his saw and cleaver.

Chapter Thirty-three

JAN 18, 1995

Dear Axel,

Our calls have been so cordial — well, that's the wrong word. They're familiar and meaningless on the surface and full of undeclared resentment underneath. I want to cut through to what used to be our rapport, our gladness in each other. I stay awake nights and cringe at the memory of my defensive barrage in Toronto re your war videos. But I don't regret it. And I saw only one tape. How badly might our love (Is that too strong? Is it only affection?) have been altered if I'd been reckless enough to view the other one? We don't mention love. If ever it should be mentioned, it's now. I don't mean to wield it, prod with it, only to make mine clear, in case you doubted, after my attack. I don't doubt yours. What I doubt is your understanding of me, of how different my life is now.

You used suffering that I'm close to here, that is part of the lives around me and impinges directly on my own mind and thoughts. You used these horrors for the small hope of gaining some emotional leverage.

Don't those pictures shock you, sicken you? I think they don't. Or you would have foreseen the impact. There is a different aspect to the image, as opposed to the fact, to simply knowing what was done. I think that was the worst thing for me — the recycling of those atrocities in a Manhattan apartment or wherever else they might be displayed for people to gape at. How is this distribution ever not a compounding of the obscenity?

I'm angry now. You're thinking: Chris is on a rant. He's not considering the right of people to know the truth, the worst. All right.

But I know it. I don't want to see it, and see it, until by some shift of consciousness I begin to imagine it can't harm me, until I view it as just another ghastly wonder of the world. Its truth is not proof of its need for reproduction. We don't need copies of these things. They reverse themselves and become real again, become acts to be copied. Men in Bosnia will repeat them in real time, on living people, in their homes, and call it some sort of historical reckoning.

You've changed my idea of you — of Axel, my dearest, oldest friend. I don't want an apology. I want a reason. Maybe I've got it wrong somehow. But you should have known. I want the reassurance that you know how much this place means to me, and that you will never toy with that connection again. And I want some regret, at least a little.

xo

Chris

FEB 15

Dear Chris,

I read your letter late yesterday and couldn't sleep. I've been staring at it today since breakfast and I'm wondering what I'm supposed to say except I'm sorry, and of course I regret that I hurt you. We don't need to say anything about love, do we? I never thought so. Of course it's there. The "gladness." That says it. And why say it at all?

But you're on a high horse. You'll have to consider this before you send off a reply. Please reread your letter and think about what you've accused me of.

You insist on regret from me. You seem to feel no regret for the last three years of separation. I miss our friendship. For you, I guess, it's on the back burner. For me it feels like it's slipping away. Your letter sometimes reads like a *pushing away*. I tossed in bed last night over the change in you, your coldness.

You say I'm not sufficiently shocked by the video record of war. I have to say that your shock is what war correspondents and people in TV news have to deal with very early in our careers — we either get over it, or we get out, or we become twisted. It's a job. I made the mistake of thinking of you for a moment as a colleague, instead of as a news outsider. You are right to say that over there you're on the inside, close to people whose lives are torn. You're on the inside of the *outer fringe* of a war. You've seen the funerals, you've seen dead Serb warriors. I knew you hadn't seen the kind of thing that's on the Zvornik tape. I wanted your response. Serbs have done the major killing in this war, and the most cleansing. They're doing more right now in Bihać and other places. You're in love with a Serb. You haven't said, but you might have some Muslim friends too. I was not sensitive to these connections when I chose the tapes and gave them to you. *I regret that*, and I won't say it again. But what's eating you up is that same knowledge, isn't it? You know what's been done by Serbs. The monks know. It's a burden. You wrote all about the guilt of people who make and distribute videos, and not a word about the guys who fired RPGs into that stairwell. I'm surprised, actually, that you're having this issue out with me (in a roundabout way) instead of with Stefan.

"Emotional leverage" is not what I hope for. It's just a little tool, and we both use it. What I hope is that you will not go into Bosnia, for any reason. I know how chummy you are with the local militia boys. And this development with Martin Ivry and the Slobodan fellow in Sarajevo, a possible Pimm connection. Toni said you want to go to some town near Goražde for birth records. Why have you kept me in the dark about this? So I wouldn't interfere? But how is concern for your safety an interference? I say just stay out. Pimm would say the same. Why do you think I haven't been to Bosnia? I watched Susan Christoff stay in bed for two months after she came home from Vareš and Stupni Do. I told them then I wouldn't go back there. Dubrovnik was enough. It's my job and I'm a coward but I don't want my mind fucked with. You think video is bad? Susan couldn't cook or eat because everything smelled to her like death.

I'm sorry. I know Stefan has family there, I know he lost his sister. I do see how involved you are. Maybe I should read Slobodan's memoir, if Ivry doesn't mind sharing him.

I know Stefan will probably keep you there. (He'll want you to steer clear of danger too.) I still can't think how you're working out the God thing. You're a pagan and always will be.

That's all. No more leverage.
Much love,
Axel

MARCH 20, 1995

Dear Toni,
We had some good news from Martin this morning. He managed to contact Brother Maksim's parents in Sarajevo. They're still in their apartment, no heat, but surviving. His father has some heart trouble. Their Croat neighbours are fetching water and firewood for them.

Slobo's doing okay, occasional migraines, but he's gained a little weight. He can't remember the stepmother's name. I also got through to Rudačac. All the registry records were amalgamated in Goražde years ago. What this means, really, is that I must make do with my imagination. I wish I could meet Slobo and talk to him.

Very glad to hear that Jelena is breaking more barriers. Sounds like her convalescence has helped keep you near your keyboard.

Axel and I are still on shaky ground. He hasn't phoned since he got the enclosed letter from me. His response is also enclosed. You can draw your own conclusions. Please don't tell him you've read this exchange. I think phone calls are out for a while. We'll let the dust settle.

Our oldest brother and former abbot, Father Vladimir, quite frail and near blind, has died. He had virtually stopped eating, then stopped getting out of bed, then one morning he was dead. He was eighty-nine, a monk since 1933. He was at Mileševa Monastery when the Nazis bombed it. There were tears here, open weeping at the funeral, the first such outpouring I've seen among the brothers. They are more stoical about other deaths. A body's death is the soul's freedom. But most funerals are in the towns, close to home. We've buried, I think, sixteen soldiers since the war began. The town parishes have easily buried hundreds.

It was so cold here last week the potatoes and turnips froze in the root cellar. Here's an image: blue-grey frozen twilight. Eight men in black coats and sheepskin gloves and hats crunching across a frozen lake, each carrying his fresh catch of trout. Little holes and stools dot the ice. An hour later we're passing steaming platters of fried fish. This on a day of fasting. Other days it's beans straight from the can. Either way, we thank God for our bounty.

xo C

Chapter Thirty-four

In April I received a thick Kušić instalment from Antonia, with a note:

Chris,

I'll refrain from comment on your tiff with Axel (I don't know where to begin), but I will say it was interesting. Something else: to say that Serbs have done the most killing in Bosnia is saying something unproven. Things are still in tremendous flux. For two years it's been largely a Croat-Muslim war, as Axel ought to know. (I do admit a small bias.)

Jelena needs only a cane to walk now. Mater wants to take her back to Trieste. I think that's fine. She'll be surrounded by aunties and will get better rehab. Nenad (her ex) showed up for a few days, cried a little, got in the way, drank all my booze and left. If she can get far away from him it will help. We had word that Stanko, their son, was wounded in Bihać, and now is in hospital in Banja Luka. It's a leg wound. We're hoping it's his ticket out. I hope he hopes the same. He has a wife and child in Trebinje.

This appears to be Slobo's last instalment. He has asked that both his original and the translation be sent to his sister in Belgrade. I've unfortunately left the first part of the translation in NY. If you still have the full English there, could you copy and send it? *Vedrana Brković: #23, Zmaj Jovina 30, Beograd.* I'll work on getting the original to her.

I feel I've not quite caught Slobo's tone in the English. The structures are so different, not just grammar and so on, but in the way his thoughts and emotions live in the words. It may just be that when I read it in Serbo-Cro it stirs different things for me.

Let me know about the copy for Vedrana.

Love,

Toni

Chapter Thirty-five

SEPTEMBER 1992

I prepared to flee my home. There was nothing to stay for in Mali Voćnjak, every reason to abandon a life that in fact could be neither abandoned nor retained, for it no longer existed. The word flight did not quite define this process. As in my childhood war, it was a dangerous trudge and stumble. If a moment of terror forced true flight, it was more like that of a fly approaching a windscreen.

The TV crew filmed me, then departed on its search for more drama, briefly capturing a tableau of corpses beside the road. I sifted through the charred debris of my roofless kitchen, a clear autumn sun casting all in stark relief. I salvaged some sardines and tinned beans, some biscuits toasted inside their burnt carton, a tough and smoky heel of bread from the breadbox, some cheese and a bottle of water from inside my scorched fridge. In the bedroom, I found Hana's old metal sewing box undamaged at the bottom of the closet. Under the felt lining were ten one hundred-Deutschmark notes, a prescient gift from my daughter Zlata some years before. From the box I also took an embroidered prayer that Zlata had begun and not completed during her teenage flaring of Muslim piety: five lines of scything Arabic script in shiny gold thread on blood-red velvet. The Arabic words were a mystery to me, but it was almost guaranteed that no Muslim warrior who stopped me on the road could better me in this. Until I reached Serb-held land, Zlata's unfinished prayer would be produced and murmured over at the first sign of thuggish threat. If Serbs were to accost me later, my father's name and my own foreskin would show my allegiance. I took with me three other objects: an old road map, a small tin box of letters going back to my childhood and my little book of poems published twenty years before in Sarajevo, poems that strived to distil transcendence from a young boy's experience in a war zone. I'd entered my burning house the day before to save it. All my other books, many burnt beyond use, were left, among them school texts and histories filled with the rousing prose of Tito's mythmakers.

I hoped to travel only by road, for the mountain paths were likely scattered with land mines, and my ignorance of the old peasant trails and their convolutions would only compound the danger. My idea was to reach Višegrad, which was said to be secure within Serbian territory. I had hardly a choice in this matter if I wished to survive. My identity papers showed my father a Serb; my sheathed penis proved me an heir of the Kosovo martyrs. Men were spared or murdered daily based on a few grams of wrinkled skin. Until the madness had spent itself, I would be a quiet Serb in a Drina River town purged of Islam. I would beg a bed or a square of floor and a blanket from other Serbs, and like them I would daily swallow and subvert my unasked-for burden of shame, and my bitterness. I would hide Zlata's prayer in my shoe or under a floorboard. This scrap of cloth was the last proof of my Hana's life long faith, which she quietly honoured in the face of my own habitual doubt. It was also the final emblem of my buried half-self, the half I was now willing to disavow to save my skin.

So this was my plan, and it began easily enough. I stepped from my doorway, crunching on shards of roof tiles, and moved down the mud ruts of Obućarska Street toward the river road. On the way, I passed some corpses, and portions of others. One was only a pelvis with bloated legs attached. Off in the weeds, I saw a chunk of meaty ribcage. I focused on the far bank of the river where willows moved placidly in the warm breeze. A young soldier stopped me as I neared the bullet-pocked sign marking the limit of Mali Voćnjak. He searched me for weaponry but did not find the Deutschmarks inside my shoes. He pawed through my bag of food and took a can of sardines, peeled it open, and began eating with his fingers. He let me pass. I walked west along the river toward Djavica, where I hoped I might cross the bridge into Serbian territory. Barring the sights that assaulted my vision, I was unmolested for the hour of this passage. Djavica was a hundred burnt houses and a few near-intact ones that quartered its Muslim liberators. Men lolled about in the sun awaiting their dinner, a sheep's carcass spitted over coals. The woolly skin was stretched on poles near the fire. Two soldiers circled each other, playing a head-slapping game, a test of agility and stamina, brotherly smiles frozen on their stung, livid faces. Weapons were everywhere handy — stuck into belts, brandished by guards on the perimeter, cradled like a lover by each drowsy fighter lounging in the trampled grass. I was only glanced at as I shuffled meekly past and approached the narrow bridge that would take me across the Jadar and to Serbian ground.

Two guards manned the checkpoint at the bridge, one paunchy and wryly watchful, the other a skinny puppy flaunting authority. My intention to cross raised one question from the earnest one: "Who are you for?" I told him I had family in Višegrad, that I was a citizen of Bosnia. The paunchy one snorted. They searched me, and the snarly pup found my Deutschmarks. He counted them. The two exchanged glances. The pup shouted to his superior, who was bent over the spitted sheep. He approached, chewing on a charred rind of meat. I was explained. My papers and Zlata's embroidered prayer were stared at, clutched in fingers slick with grease.

"Show your cock," said the leader. They crowed with derision at my poor shrivelled cock. The leader touched the muzzle of his pistol to it. "I could trim it for you. Or should we call the Mullah?" More hooting laughter. He buttoned my one thousand Deutschmarks into his breast pocket then moved his sweating face close to mine. "Go," he said. "Go to your Chetnik pussy-brothers. And beg Allah to forgive you." He drew back and ceremoniously extended my prayer to me, a sardonic gift to a man bound for hell. Then his gun urged me forward.

I stepped onto the worn wooden planking of the bridge. It was perhaps thirty metres to the far side. And there were the Serbs, watching me from their own checkpoint. Beyond them were some U.N. vehicles among the trees, and the blue helmets of peacekeepers. I moved ahead, the Serb guards steadily following my approach, the Muslim eyes behind me boring into my back. And at the centre of the bridge the shouting began from both sides.

First Serbs: "Halt, *balija!* Don't move! Drop your bags!"

Then Muslims: "He's nothing! He's a Yugoslav!" Laughter. "He's for Comrade Tito! Shoot him, Chetniks! Shoot the fucking Commie!"

Waves of laughter assailed my back. I stood with hands above my head, still clutching Zlata's velvet prayer. Then the shooting began and I was flat against the dusty planks staring between them at the flowing river below. Shooting and shouting rolled over me as I lay quaking and saw a flash of red and gold falling away, touching the muddy water, then sliding smoothly from my sight. And then I felt ready to die there in the hail of fire. In a flash I saw it as inevitable, my perfect death, midway across this bridge between my selves, each half flinging bullets and extravagant insults across the void. But the gunfire stopped. It came to me that there had been no hits. No clang from the steel beams of the bridge, no splintered wood flying at my face. They were only having frisky boyish fun at my expense, wasting bullets at the sky.

So I was forced to carry on. There was a silence, as if all present were allowing a moment to savour my predicament. I struggled to order my mind and calm myself, and soon the taunts and catcalls resumed. Keeping my head down I raised my palms in submission. More shooting, very brief, and more laughter. And as it faded, a sonorous Serb voice rolled across the bridge, expressing hope that Allah would insert every past and future Muslim turd into every dead and living Muslim mother's pussy. The Muslims went wild, hurling lead across the bridge in a sustained barrage. Now the steel trusses rang, and the deflected bullets splintered the planking around me and cut through the water below. When at last the din stopped, a new voice resonated from among the Serbs, in peculiar Serbo-Croatian: "Hold your fires!

You are burning down and you begin to think now, beside you are killing here old man! Important?"

I peeked at the far side and saw a U.N. blue-helmet standing at the entrance to the bridge. He began to walk toward me with a measured and confident gait. The only sound now was his footsteps on the bridge and the murmuring flow of the river. He bent to retrieve my scattered bags. On his shoulder was the crest of his nation's flag: a red leaf on white with red borders. The Canadian leaned over me: "You are injury?" I considered, and guessed that I was not. He helped me to my feet. I could see that he had officer's stripes, though he seemed hardly more than a boy to me. He led me across to the other side and exchanged some tense words with the Serb guards. Bearded militiamen were milling about still erupting with obscenities for the Muslims. The U.N. officer hovered while the guards perused my ID papers and I stuttered my intention to reach Višegrad. They pushed the papers back at me without comment. Their pressing need was to heave more lead across the bridge. I walked away from the guards and the Canadian, forcing resolve and purpose into my trembling step, while behind me their renewed dispute grew in volume and misunderstanding. Under the trees along the road, U.N. soldiers in fresh uniforms leaned against their clean tanks and APCs, cradling their oiled weapons. Some of them greeted me in passing. "*Sretno!*" they said jauntily. Good luck! The United Nations had intervened on my behalf — and without firing a single shot. Carefully adhering to his Rules of Engagement, my foreign saviour helped me across a bridge like a perfect Boy Scout, after I had the amazing good fortune not to be riddled with bullets before his eyes.

But it is not for me, a village postmaster, to second-guess the policies of peacemakers. Being from far away, they naturally have a superior grasp of a land they've never inhabited. My duty, indeed, is to thank them. The polite young officer even carried my bags for me! And no proud victim evades his measure of guilt. My own people have perhaps made guilt the most fluid and least understood of emotions. It is our subconscious-permeating ether. We can't escape it. In peace it invisibly surrounds us; in battle it catches fire and fuels us. Tito's own fire was a sacrosanct enforcement and recycling of others' guilt. His prisons transformed heroes into criminals, then released them to become leaders. Yet nearly all of us, if only in brief moments, have deeply mourned our Tata Tito, and wanted him back.

I followed the river east now, retracing my steps on new ground. Through the trees on the far bank, I again saw the remains of Djavica. A moment later something cut through the bushes behind me and I heard a distant *crack* from across the water. A second bullet zinged past so close to my face that I felt its sizzle on the air, and then I was hit in the neck and thrown to the ground. I put a hand to my throat and felt the hot blood spurting through my fingers. My vision blurred and went black, and the next morning a unit of passing Serbs searched my corpse for valuables before tossing it into the river.

That did not happen. What happened was that I found the road leading south, toward Višegrad, and walked another hour until the sun was almost behind the hills. Seeing a lone ruined house at the end of a meadow, I made for it, thinking I would hide and take shelter for the night. I peered through the open doorway. There was no sound but that of a few crickets warming to the night. I crossed the threshold, failing to notice a thin wire stretched low across the doorframe. There was a deafening explosion and I was thrown through the air. I lay on the ground with a great roaring in my head and saw in the dry grass, at an unlikely remove, a leg with shreds of trouser, and a bloody hand, poised as if to accept a gift.

But this is what actually happened: I walked until dusk, wolfed down some sardines and beans and slept on some straw in a cowshed. I woke early and set out, my old body complaining bitterly. About midday I came upon three soldiers at a table in the dirt yard outside a tavern. One called me from the road. "Come here old one, or we'll shoot your ears off!"

I approached.

"Sit!"

Like an obedient dog I sat on the wooden bench.

"Drink!"

He slid a bottle toward me. I drank. The bottle contained brandy that might have been kerosene for the vile taste.

"What is your name?"

"Slobodan."

"Freedom! Freedom for all Serbs! What is your story, Slobo?"

"May I know your name first?"

"You may! So polite, this motherfucker. My name is Ratko. Not Mladić. I am Ratko Mistić, of Glavčice. You know it?"

"I'm sorry."

"On the main road above Zvornik. Near Janja."

"Ah yes."

"Your story!"

"I am the former postmaster of Mali Voćnjak. Near nowhere."

"Hah! And what did the Turks do to you?"

"They killed Prince Lazar."

"They did! Fuck them in the ass!"

"My story ... is that men came to my village and drove out the Muslims."

"Freedom!"

"Then Muslims came and drove out the Serbs. Now there is nobody."

"Fuckers! May they die in agony!"

"Excuse me ... Ratko ..."

"Slobo!"

"I have a question."

"Ask! Ask anything."

"I think I drove once through Glavčice."

"Sneeze and you will miss it."

"I recall a memorial at a crossroads."

"Memorial?"

"A monument, on the road to a monastery."

"Tavna Monastery. We saved it from the *balije*."

"Surely they were too busy running to be a threat."

"We had them running like rabbits!"

"This monument was for dead Partisans. It was a red granite star."

"That thing? It's good only for target practice!"

"But so many died for that freedom, Ratko, for Yugoslavia."

"Oy yoy! Slobo! You are still a fucking Yugoslav? You need your head fixed. But first we need another bottle! Zoran!"

A voice answered from the dark hole of the tavern entrance. Then a bottle arrived in the hand of a fat man who smelled sweet, like rotting meat. Over his belly was stretched a stained Chicago Bulls T-shirt. He withdrew.

"Drink, Slobo!"

"Thank you, Ratko. I would offer the next round, but ..."

"But you can't pay with blood."

"Not for brandy at least."

"Not even for this horse piss!"

We drank, passing the bottle round. I contrived to drink thimblefuls. The two younger soldiers were all but mute, content to bask in Ratko's performance and nod pie-eyed agreement.

"Slobo, listen to me now. Everyone! Listen! There was never a race of South Slavs! It was invented by politicians. This is the lie that killed us. What happened was this: Tito died. And Yugoslavia died."

"That's all?"

"That is everything."

"But Ratko, he had to die. He was not a god."

"He was a living god. Of course he was. Everywhere his picture hung in the highest spot. Like Jesus."

"You're only mocking."

"Not at all! Tito performed miracles. He beat the Germans and Italians. He made us stop fighting with ourselves. He was brave and smart. He fought like a lion. He became wily like an old lion. You saw the shrewdness in his face. Then he died, and Croats and *balije* saw their chance. No more Daddy to tell them who they could not push around, so they began to steal from us and murder us all over again. They will never learn. So fuck them. Fuck them with razors. We can never live with them again. May every Croat and Muslim die. May they die as my brother Serbs died in the hills above Brezanac, with pitchforks through their eyes and their mouths full of shit. May they die with their livers roasting before their eyes. May all Muslims and Croats die in ways worse than these. May they be skinned slowly from the toes up and roasted on spits turned by their mothers and grandmothers. Shoot their cocks off first. Pull out their lying tongues. Feed them dog shit and broken glass. Blowtorch their fucking eyeballs until their brains melt and run out through their ears. Fuck them! Fuck them in the ass with cannons! They are animals!"

Ratko stared at me with a crazed, absent look. Then he brought both fists down hard on the table. The bottle tottered and he grabbed at it, steadied it, held it there, his eyes fixed on the silvery liquid.

"My head is going to split with this war. It's like an axe in my brain! The worst is that they have made me this, have made me a man burning up inside. It's like a cancer eating me. They have done this to me. Now I want to fuck them. I want to watch them squirm. It was only an idle thought before. Now I'm a killer. So roast them alive. Let them scream. It is sweet music to my ears."

Ratko drank. The bottle was passed round.

"Now Slobo, you must confess. Do you hate them too? You must take an oath."

"I hate the Muslims who killed my friend Mihajlo."

"They must die as he died."

"I also hate the Serbs who killed my Muslim friends, my neighbours who were good people, who harmed no one. Our children played together. A Muslim doctor presided over my son's birth."

I don't know what impulse made me say to a crazed Serb that I could hate Serbs. It came out of me. Then I watched as from a distance to know my fate. The young ones froze. Ratko's eyes gazed at me uncomprehending, then with a groping sort of look he raised the bottle. I thought he would smash it across my face but he only took a long swig and replaced it delicately on the table.

"You had Muslim friends. That does not make you different. It does not make you an exception. That is past. Pfft! All gone. We're at war. So wake up. Wake up, you stupid cunt! You must never say anything against Serbs. You who are a Serb. Get away from us now. Go. Go!"

I stood.

"Run! Fucking Yugoslav pussy! Run fast or we'll shoot!"

I ran.

At a hamlet called Odrodići, the road ended. A packed-earth trail climbed into thickly wooded hills. The houses were intact. Children played in the yards. I called to a woman taking in her laundry. She only continued her task, darkly eyeing my approach with her mouth full of pegs. I wanted to know if the trail would take me to a road that led to Višegrad. She freed her tongue. "The trail goes to Virmanice, on the Brložnik road. From there you must ask someone else."

"Many thanks! And, please, I was hoping I might find some shelter for tonight. I've had a difficult trek."

A silence as she violently reeled in socks and underpants. Then she turned and called into the house.

"Dragan! Dragan get off your behind and come talk to this man!"

Dragan appeared. He listened to my story of woe and invited me inside. Slivovitz was served and we exchanged news. The brandy soon left me helpless against exhaustion. Dragan led me to a small room with a bed: a boy's room, with soccer posters and pictures of motorcycles. He left me and I sank onto the mattress. My twitching eyelids closed and finally I dozed, adrift in a madhouse of images from the day and the previous weeks. Then I was thrashing awake from a dream of fire and knives piercing me. I lay there in the silence and finally gave in to tears, quietly so as not to disturb.

They later gave me a meal, and the next morning some bread and tea. I was sent on my way with a few apples and a full bottle of water. The well-used trail wound upwards through the trees, far along the bare crest of a ridge, then zig-zagged down to a narrow valley with a bubbling stream and lush oaks and maples. There were no signs of the war here. I came to a gravel road and saw houses at a far bend. From Virmanice, I followed the twisting road southwards.

At Brložnik, a convoy of French aid workers offered me a ride. They hoped to negotiate their way past Serb lines to deliver food and medicine to Žepa. They left me where the road forked into two river gorges, with a thick bar of chocolate in my hand. Now I passed isolated houses, empty and staring like ghosts. I had not been in these mountains since we'd trundled through them with Žepa's mullah in 1941. Perhaps I was on the same road, now spread with gravel but otherwise unchanged. It is still said that Žepa's landscape is so remote and forbidding only wolves make love there. The plunging ravines, the streams in deep cuts of rock, the hope of respite in Višegrad, it all raised memories and made time seem compressed, or as if it had never advanced.

I passed a second night in a Serb home, well fed despite their evident lack. That same sunny afternoon I stepped onto the cobblestones of Mehmed Pasha's bridge on the Drina, and observed among rooftops at its far end the square white bell tower and modest onion domes of an Orthodox church. Višegrad's other towers, my Muslim starships, were absent. The town appeared otherwise intact, and strangely quiet. Reaching the broad stone tablet at the bridge's centre, I looked up at the indecipherable Turkish inscription and saw it backdropped by hills whose shapes were stamped in my memory: green pyramid on one side, craggy knobs on the other; between them the blue-green Drina swirling down from Foča and Goražde. I had driven through Višegrad many times on the main road and over the modern highway bridge, travelling in summer with Hana and our children to visit her brother in Foča. But I'd not stood on Mehmed Pasha's bridge since 1944. I was twelve. Italy had been long defeated and the Germans were in grudging retreat from Bosnia. Višegrad was then a crumbling Chetnik stronghold awaiting the belated attack that would secure it for the Partisans. And Aunt's determination to move us to her childhood home in Serbian Priboj was on the verge of fruition.

I had unremembered this Drina Bridge. I pushed it below thought each time I passed near it or overheard reference to its legend, a legend inseparable from the Nobel Prize that for a few moments in 1961 thrust blinking Yugoslavia into the world's spotlight. When Marko and Zlata brought home the newly famous novel from school, the epic tale of bridge and river (link and divide, both well tainted with every effluent a corpse can provide), a tale that dutiful Yugoslavs publicly embraced, while others found in it grave ethnic slurs, when this fraught and lauded narrative appeared among school texts on our kitchen table, reviving in my mind its implications, it was for me only a thing again to be avoided; my Višegrad had been wilfully buried. I have called myself a Yugoslav and a Bosnian, but for decades I shunned this required text. Then at the age of thirty, a village postman-poet traipsing around Belgrade on a holiday weekend, towing my indulgent Hana, I entered a bookstore and there was Ivo Andrić, new bard to the world, his image arrayed before us on countless new volumes of *The Bridge on the Drina*. No book, not any Tito tome, had ever been so prominent. This novel, which had gathered dust on shelves since 1945, was now a shining beacon for South Slav pride. The world had informed us of its worth. In that flush of pride I bought the book, and on the return train to peasant Bosnia, I read it to the close of chapter three and the famous impaling, that passage of shimmering brutality that makes school-girls feel ill and boys crow with pleasure, and then I closed the book and failed, for thirty years, to read further. Andrić's Višegrad seemed far too much like the one I knew.

NOVEMBER 1941

News came over the mountains from Serbia to Žepa. Germans had murdered two thousand at Kraljevo, nearly three thousand at Kragujevac. Now Chetniks were attacking Partisans at Užice, dashing the tenuous hope that they might stay united against the

Fascist invaders. In a country overrun by alien devils, we were now to be entertained by our quarrelling brothers, the enemy recast as a useful tool for leveraging Royalist or Titoist advantage.

In our Žepa camp, the women muttered over their cookfires and cast their eyes heavenward as the old men raised their voices in disputes over duty and honour. Why fling bullets for Tito? Why for King Petar? Which choice was the betrayal of all Serbs, which the only hope? And the question too terrible to voice, yet lurking under every other: whose sons were braving the real enemy's bullets, and whose were mere dupes or brainless zealots firing upon their proper allies, spilling their own precious blood?

If Chetniks and Partisans could by their petty squabbling collude in the desecration of their ancient shared land merely for the frail hope of some future advantage, then where was the end? Wasn't it painfully obvious that Croats were the clear and present devils, the true black sheep of our divided family? Have we not all heard of or known — known brutally — the revolting crimes of the Ustasha death squads? Now the Krauts are matching them in blood-frenzy. No surprise. It's never been a secret that the second language of Zagreb is German; of Dubrovnik and Split, Italian. Croats bartered away their Slav inheritance decades ago. So let them all move to Trieste and bloat themselves on pasta. Let every Zagreb puppet Nazi choke on fat tasteless sausage and pastry *mit schlag*. Let us push them out of our house, through the door they have forever darkened with theft and butchery, and swiftly change the locks so they can never re-enter to further pollute our imperilled Serbian stock.

And we must also admit that the Partisans themselves are riddled with Croats. Like tainting weevils in a flour bin, slowly consuming its goodness and leaving only shit. The Partisan camp

is nothing but a den of misfits and opportunists, a false brotherhood for those unfortunates who imagine they can deny their
own ancestry with impunity for the sake of a glittering idea, and
a strange one at that, claiming that all men are equal and that
workers and peasants can somehow muddle through without
kings, without great men to inspire them and defend them from
foreign evils. This communal fantasy, this airy high-flown God-
rejecting fairy tale of comradeship, by calling itself Partisan, only
reveals its patent absurdity: it is a new Apartism, a corrupting
haven for all who are Yugoslav only by a habit of residence, by an
accident of some past migration from elsewhere. So Tito's slavish
army is naturally filled with mere proximate Yugoslavs, those
who are present but of no discernable South Slav legitimacy: the
Muslims, Jews, Slovenes and Vojvodina Hungarians, the Montenegrin mountain people who cannot even sign their names. This
ragtag band can have no anthem, cannot even raise a common
voice. They are the enemy as surely as the Croats, Germans or
Italians. And this leaves but one answer. We must raise our glass
only to King Petar, to our Chetniks who are the only pure Serb
warriors, purely and honourably engaged in defence of our
ancient land, and to their brave commander Draža Mihailović
the single untainted leader and future hope of our Serb Kingdom,
which is the last fortress of authentic South Slav blood and honour.
Our Chetniks in Užice only followed the hard law of neccessity,
saw clearly that their battle was on two fronts, against two deadly
forces: Fascism and Communism, each of them rife with intrud-
ers from other lands and with traitors from within. These forces,
make no mistake, are the greatest threat to our people since the
murder of Lazar. Without the complete commitment and unity
of Serbs against these evils, the Serbian Nation will die.

Of course, none of our old ones argued with quite the same words; these phrases came later, in abundance, from a roadside orator. But the shifting forces of war and fear and village prejudice worked together in our Žepa camp only to further enhance our sense of beseiged Serbness, and our hopes for the Chetniks. The resulting consensus, though tacit and never proclaimed, was that Tito was a traitor, and the Chetniks were our boys rallied against old brutalities and new, incomprehensible politics. Those who had sons or brothers (or daughters, or sisters) bearing arms for Tito now kept it to themselves. My father was now fully unmentionable. For all we knew he had been hurling return fire at the Chetniks on the day they attacked Užice.

The man who did frame our dilemma in those charged words, playing on old legends, on bigotry and desperation, spoke them standing on a flat plinth of rock one clear and crisp November afternoon. Behind him, flaming maples and sumacs lent their fire to his rhetoric. Days of dry air and sunshine had spurred migration. The roads and trails were filled with refugees seeking a haven in which to survive the winter. For us and many other Serbs this meant Višegrad. Word had spread that its occupying Ustashas had been replaced by an Italian garrison. With control of the town and its bridge, the Italians were content to sit tight and not risk their advantage. Meanwhile, Chetniks entrenched in the surrounding hills refrained from attacks on troops who'd brought order to the town and stopped the Croat abuse of Serb civilians. The situation offered tolerable refuge from increasingly ruthless Krauts and Ustashas. Serbs were now being allowed to cross Italian lines and enter or leave Višegrad to join relatives or return to their homes. Muslim families trapped in the town were allowed out, though many chose to stay, while some returned to their villages only to be chased off or killed by newly militant Serbs who'd been their neighbours. This was the precarious situation that we trudged toward that day in early November, leaving behind remote Žepa where winter would surely have seen us starve, and hoping for a welcome from Aunt's kinfolk in the town on the Drina. She was not even sure of their street address.

At Klašnik on our first day of walking, we encountered the roadside orator rallying Serbs for King Petar. I recall him distinctly, a young bearded beanstalk of a man with wire spectacles. His long-fingered hands planed through the air as the stirring phrases left his lips. He wore a dark fur cap and an old army jacket with brass buttons, the double eagle sewn to the breast pocket, and when it gaped open a black pistol could be seen strapped at his side. A small crowd had gathered near him in the sun; not quite around him, which would imply real interest, but near enough to catch his words and be distracted from their cares. It was an excuse to stop and rest, to sit on a rock or log and gnaw on a stale crust, roll a precious cigarette or slip behind a bush for relief. Yet people were compelled to admiration. They watched the eloquent hands shaping history and the future, and their heads would tilt with the shifts of argument. Others listened with eyes drifting over the blazing hillsides, the sloping scraps of spent cornfield, and their gaze spiralled inward, as if they heard only a reminder of mortality before which there was no hope of protest. But the eloquent Chetnik appeared charged with life, fully grappling with the danger and challenge of it, with the call to duty and to responsibility for the future. At the end there was a scattering of weak applause from some, while others simply began hoisting bags and gathering children to move on. The speaker leapt from his boulder and approached the knots of exhausted nomads.

That such energy, such pitch of argument should be spent on an accidental gathering of overburdened women, gouty oldies and dirty children seemed almost ridiculous. It took barely a moment's reflection to feel behind the stirring phrases a familiar hopelessness: here again we were offered more reasons to betray our friends and neighbours and our own families, and have ourselves killed in the process.

Now the Chetnik was approaching Uncle Vaso, who at once erupted with a violent hacking and dredging up of mucus. The Chetnik proffered a precious Belgrade cigarette. Uncle rasped and swallowed and accepted. The two men lit up and puffed seriously, gazing at separate hilltops. Uncle spat a thick green wad into the dust.

"Sir. That cough must be dealt with. We have an excellent doctor in our camp at Pozderčići."

"Please, you needn't call me 'sir.' I am Vaso Kušić."

"A pleasure, Vaso. And I am Živko Uskorović."

"My pleasure, Živko. Long life to King Petar."

"Let us hope, Vaso."

"I hope every day. We all hope and pray each day for Serb victory."

"This goes without saying. But Vaso ..." Here the Chetnik paused, narrowing his eyes at the horizon. "Hope and prayers alone are worse than useless. Forgive my bluntness, but we must all face this squarely. Hope is a state of inaction. Hope, in plain fact, is next to cowardice. I don't say that you are a coward, Vaso. Don't mistake me. I say only that your present situation — walking from here to there with the hope of staying out of trouble until men of action save your hide from the Fascist and Communist dogs — is in one sense only a passive form of desertion. You do not actually run from the enemy, but that is only because you have never actually engaged him. Your absence from the conflict works only for the enemy. Every man who can carry a gun and doesn't will bear not only the conqueror's yoke, but also the knowledge of his own guilt if this war is lost. May I ask, Vaso, how you have served the cause of Serb freedom in this war?"

"How I served? I served twenty-five years ago, Živko. This is God's truth. Can you imagine how? Do you know a little Serbian history? I stopped an Austrian bullet at Obrenovac. We drove them back across the Sava. They jumped into the river and left their wounded to rot. I sucked chlorine gas into my lungs at Čačak. I have served. And look, look what it did to me! I'm an old man at forty-eight! And you call me a coward?" The Chetnik was silent now, frowning at the treetops. "I only mean to say, Živko, that you've met a man with some scars. And now if you don't mind, I'm taking my family on to Višegrad, where we have kinfolk waiting. I wish you every success in finding men who will fight as we did for Serb freedom. My force has been spent. I'm no good for fighting now. One tumble into a ditch and you'd have to leave me to the wolves."

"No Chetnik would leave you to the wolves, Vaso."

"Well, I will save you the decision."

With this Uncle carefully nipped the ember from his cigarette and put the unburned portion into his pocket, and we prepared to move on. His performance had been unexpected. Even Aunt had ceased her endless fidgeting to stare at him with pride. This man who seemed to me inept and clownish had perhaps been a proper soldier. I see now that Uncle was brandishing the flag of honour at a difficult moment. But his flash of indignation, the way his face hardened and his voice shook in the effort of control — the moment stays with me.

I'd been told of Uncle's war service, which my younger father had escaped. I'd heard cousin Željko's indifferent words about Germans and gas when I'd asked why Uncle spat so much. None of it hit home until I saw him reduce the eloquent Chetnik to the status of an unschooled yapping puppy. This did not make Uncle in any way exceptional to other men, but it revised my callow child's judgements. It changed what I saw reflected in his eyes.

Underneath Uncle's words to the Chetnik was the memory of my mother's death, and its poisoning of our minds to the Royalist cause. It was why Father was now with Tito, and why Uncle's proud memories of his Serb Army service against Austro-German aggression were now blurred by his contempt for the new Serbianism forced upon us that brilliant fall day by the young orator. Muslim nomads too were passing through Klašnik that day, unobtrusively lugging their burdens, hoping not to betray their fear to this firebrand, breathing the miasma of his contempt. They heard him define their guilt: "Just as the Jews crucify Christ with every devotion, so too does each Muslim prayer drive a knife through the soul of Saint Prince Lazar." As if God were no more than the revered prince of one ill-used tribe. Or as if the bones of Lazar would someday rise and lead all Serbs to Paradise, leaving the rest of the world damned.

When my mother had been taken from us that spring, when all we had left of her was a broken market basket and a clot of blood at the roadside, Uncle had sat at our kitchen table, his face a carved mask as he watched Father pacing and raging, swearing at God and pounding the tabletop with fists already raw from hitting walls and trees. With eyes flat and cold as coins, Uncle gazed at his young brother, half-mad with grief and hatred of men who murder their neighbours. Uncle rolled a cigarette and methodically smoked it. He pondered the shuddering tabletop, lifted his gaze to consider the ceiling or the faraway trees beyond the window. From the shadow of the kitchen doorway, I observed this strange scene, shaking with fear and confusion, my tears a scalding river. Food and brandy sat untouched on the table. Aunt stood by the drainboard, her face creased in misery. Her gaze would light on Father's face then veer away. He was too terrible to witness. Uncle poured himself some brandy and downed it. He told Father to sit down and Father seemed not to hear him. "Sit, Davor. It's enough now. Sit and eat. Sit down!" Father stared blankly. He wrenched the chair out and sat, and seemed to alter, to redirect his thoughts, but he was only staring into the inferno inside himself. He began to speak of the things that must be done, the blood justice, his fist striking out the brutal rhythms, making the plates dance. The brandy bottle toppled. Uncle righted the bottle. He stood and reached across with both hands, grabbed Father's flayed fists and wrestled them to the tabletop, sending crockery flying. Father's eyes blazed at Uncle's face. For a moment I thought brother would kill brother. Then Father's face emptied of rage, and slowly crumpled into purest sorrow. He lowered his forehead onto the joined hands. The air seemed to ring with silence before his sobs broke, and filled the house.

Now we drew near to Višegrad. Rain held off, but clouds shadowed the hills like a grey blanket. Winter was palpable in the wind sweeping down the Drina Valley. The rutted road leading us south displayed scattered wrecked vehicles, burnt tanks, and the crude crosses and plain uprights marking recent death; here and there were horses, at every stage of decay, some butchered for food. At Sase we were stopped by Italians and searched for weapons. Asked our place of refuge in Višegrad, Uncle looked at Aunt and she smoothly lied, "Holy Virgin Church," a credible destination even had the soldiers been Belgraders rather than indifferent *paisanos*. Passing lightly damaged houses in the town's outskirts we came to a plain girdered bridge across the Rzav, and more armed guards who, after some cursory questions, let us cross into the Old Town.

We were at once treated to the sight of Italian and Ustasha officers passing by in two staff cars, the Italians imperiously in the lead. The cars stopped ahead of us and their drivers hurried round to open doors and salute as the brass disembarked and stiffly mounted the steps of a public building. The four officers turned and posed in a tableau of victors' camaraderie while a man began to take photos. As we drew near, one flicked his wrist testily — *basta!* — and the four spun on their high boots and entered the building.

Višegrad presented a tattered shuffling throng. The town market seemed spread throughout the streets. Grizzled peasants smoked next to carts and wagons full of onions, potatoes, plums and apples, wrinkled red peppers, heaps of withering corn. Women browsed with a stern eye, sniffed melons and peeled back corn husks, called sharply to drifting youngsters. The farmers nodded over their produce, offered neutral greetings to both ambling soldiers and babushkas. Calloused hands reached to turn bruised items to advantage or split open a cob for inspection.

Children hovered glumly or darted about in aimless activity. One ragged older boy came up to me and said something I couldn't catch, his odd dialect and brashness confusing me, then he pulled a fresh packet of chewing gum from his pocket. It was Italian gum, the wrapper bright red and green. He wasn't offering it, only wanting me to follow him somewhere. Then he gave up on me and moved on with a sour look. Aunt was by then at my side, yanking my arm and telling me to stay close. She barked at Vedrana and my cousins, herding us before her like dithering sheep. Moving toward the main square we passed more vendors, selling bundles of stove wood, homemade brandy, cigarettes and an array of grimy household things, even old pails and scrub-brushes, fire-scorched pots, crates full of plates and cups and empty bottles. Down the side streets, I caught glimpses of a broad ribbon of water. When we reached the square, there before us was Mehmed Pasha's bridge backdropped by soaring hills, the Drina sliding toward us under stone arches marching away to the far bank.

This was the town that would rule our lives for three years. Amid adversity, it sported an air of fraught and venal prosperity. War had no power over the sky or the bounty that nature created that year in eastern Bosnia. Those peasants in the terraced hills who'd eluded the war's scourge had gathered bumper harvests. When the region stabilized, they began their trips to market. As November unfolded and brought more and more refugees, Višegrad grew full to bursting with fugitives who could hardly find a place to lay their heads yet remained reasonably well fed. The Italian garrison requisitioned vast quantities of food, yet still there was corn, barley, potatoes and onions, even bread from the bakery. As winter set in and autumn's plenty dwindled, rationing was introduced, so that even the poorest of the poor were at least kept from starvation.

As dusk approached that first day, Aunt sent us to gawk on the bridge with Uncle while she climbed through the streets to the main church in the hope that an old priest or parishioner might know where to find her cousin Cvijeta Divjak. She had already searched for the house she recalled from girlhood visits, which she'd thought was on the hill behind the square. But the house she'd knocked at was crammed to bursting with Muslims, as were most others on the street. She returned from the church with news that a Blagoje Divjak lived in a house on the river. We were to cross the bridge and follow the road to a lane dropping down toward the water. We found the big square house of yellow stucco, built into gently sloping ground facing the Drina's pebbled bank: two floors, two attic dormers looking over the river toward the town, four stone steps rising to a broad oak door. We stood and gaped a little, then we found the kitchen door and Uncle knocked, clearing his throat.

Aunt's cousin Cvijeta was indeed the wife of this Blago Divjak, a coffee and sugar merchant. Cvijeta fluttered, bewildered about our diffident and shuffling forms, serving us some coffee and pastries. Then she knocked at Blago's office door in the rear of the house. His dark-suited bulk approached from a hallway. He had a notable stomach, one that implied a sphere of influence. Cvijeta had evidently pulled him from important work. He appeared to be in the midst of a vexing calculation, barely glanced at us as he moved to the oak sideboard and cut a pastry, stuffing half of it into his mouth while he poured himself coffee, spooned sugar, stirred. Regarding us from the corner of his eye, he crammed the remainder of the dry pastry into his mouth, wet the whole with a big gulp of coffee and settled to chewing. He half-turned and examined us with barely concealed distaste, stroking pastry flakes from his moustache and grey-streaked beard. When he'd fully chewed and swallowed, his eyes shifted decisively to Cvijeta, who at last spoke, flitting bird-like, tentative, but firm in her position of familial duty.

"Blago, this is my cousin Marija and her dear family. They have walked from Kupojno. Beyond Zenica. My dear cousin Mara. I can hardly believe it!" Here she turned to drink in Aunt's bedraggled form as if it were a reviving vision. "I've not seen her for ... it's over twenty years. They've lost their home. God be praised they are still alive. It's a miracle they found their way unharmed."

Blago poured more coffee and took another pastry, smearing it hastily with jam. He turned to exit, saying as he went, "Have Rade prepare the upper rooms."

A door closed. Cvijeta called, "You must speak to Azzopardi! We'll need extra supplies!"

Blago replied, a muffled echo, "Yes, yes! In the morning!"

Cvijeta apologized for the stale pastries. They had arrived with a load of several hundred delivered to her kitchen by an Italian truck. Dozens had been given away to neighbours. In this house we soon became used to mysterious and inappropriate abundance.

To Blago Divjak there was of course no mystery at all, but only a necessarily compromised negotiation with the shifting winds of the war economy. These dessicated sweet buns baked under requisition in Belgrade or Sarajevo had over the course of a few mysterious barters finally found their way to the Divjak kitchen, deemed an adequate recompense to a useful Serb who knew where to find real coffee and had the sense to peddle it to the men who had stolen his city. That first night Cvijeta dumped some of the remaining pastries into a large bowl, soaked them with water overnight, and next morning mixed them with cornmeal into a batter and we had griddle cakes. We stuffed ourselves, hardly believing that we had stumbled onto such bounty.

Most of our food, firewood and other supplies arrived in vehicles driven by Italian soldiers: different soldiers, different vehicles, varied quantities of a peculiar range of foodstuffs. God knows what, aside from sugar and coffee, Blago was supplying to the Italian command of Višegrad. But we comfortably survived that first frigid winter while others crammed into Višegrad's cellars and cow sheds saw the abundance of October and November disappear. Meagre subsistence became the best they could hope for. Hundreds froze or succumbed to the typhus that swept through the town in February. In our house on the river, we could see from our upper windows the pine-box coffins stacked on a patch of flat ground above the far bank, the frozen dead kept from predators by coils of barbed wire, awaiting thawed ground and enough healthy gravediggers to put them into the earth. When wood became more precious than the dignity of souls, the dead were found dumped from their coffins in the night, and wagons began carting fresh and mouldering bodies alike to a pit behind Vidova Mountain, where an imam or a priest or both together would murmur as the corpses tumbled over each other to their commingled rest.

We had no need to cross the bridge and see the town's misery. We stayed in or near the yellow house, boiled our water or melted snow, and existed on our strange forced diet. For a few weeks we would live on powdered eggs and cornmeal. Then it would be powdered eggs and tinned olives, or a big, oily wheel of parmesan, or dried pea-beans, or nothing but tins of fish or fatty pork. We grew to despise turnip, our only sure vegetable, served from a great waxy heap in the cellar. Once a live pig was delivered; Rade butchered it, and we feasted. Cvijeta took some lesser cuts to the nearest neighbours, but the rest was stored frozen under the back porch and the wealth stretched as long as possible.

Blago would come and go, sometimes returning with rare treats: hard candy or chewing gum or even chocolate. Cvijeta seemed glad to fuss over her new brood, while Blago, though gruff and preoccupied, was rarely violent. They had two sons who'd joined the Partisans that summer, their status long unknown, and a daughter who'd been with relatives in Belgrade during the spring invasion, and had stayed on there. Tempers in the house would flare in difficult times, and it was sometimes whispered that Azzopardi, the garrison commander, had been testy with Blago, that things could turn abruptly unpleasant, that we'd be reduced to standing in line at the rationing depot or living entirely on turnip and cattle corn. But that did not happen. We had in the context of that sorry place a life of ease, even of luxury. The Žepa feedmill seemed in memory like a pitiful slum. When spring came and an east wind brought the stench of decay and misery from across the Drina, we left our windows closed.

In April, an offensive by Germans and Ustashas uprooted countless more peasants. From villages and mountain hamlets in a vast tract of land stretching from Višegrad to Žepa and west to Sarajevo, they swarmed toward the Drina, fleeing murderous Ustasha units. Word came that on the banks of the Drina north of Višegrad, five hundred defenseless Serbs were butchered. Ustasha troops did not subsequently show up in Višegrad, but soon a few Germans did — officers and their retinue — and they strutted like comic-opera brigadiers, just as legend has it. They were worse in their ramrod posturing than the Italians, who at least knew how to loosen with drink. That spring Blago would come home from his meetings with Azzopardi, ripe as a spoiled pear with the scent of brandy, and we children would gape at his new talent for mimicry. A German colonel had somehow struck Blago's buried funny bone. At supper, with a boiled potato skewered on his fork, he would suddenly stiffen and point his chin at Cvijeta and bray in mock-German, "Dear wife! These potatoes gravely insult der Führer! We must at once grow new ones!" Uncle, recalling the Hapsburg Austrians, would choke with laughter.

But Germans provided a fresh market. New goods and foodstuffs came to the house as Blago further eroded his own dignity, his very right to call himself Serb or Yugoslav, in exchange for the favour of Colonel Schmundt. (When I think on it now, I feel at once contempt for this betrayal of his people, and gratitude for what he risked to feed our family. The contradiction defies resolution.) Not even the German and Italian armies combined could drink all the plundered slivovitz of Yugoslavia. Stocks of it began arriving at our back door and the crates of litre bottles were stacked in the cellar. Poor dull-witted Rade was beaten one night by Blago for stealing a bottle, and Cvijeta suffered a torrent of invective for trying to intervene. I'd never heard such language, even from Uncle. We were all grim and silent the next morning. For days Blago carried on with a show of indifference as Rade limped about. But now we were eating bacon and Dalmatian ham, fresh eggs and butter on our bread. And Blago's ire seemed only to increase with our abundance.

By May, the typhus had spent itself. On sunny mornings, Uncle took us into the town. We made the rounds of market stalls scattered with objects that desperation had rendered expendable. The array hardly changed from day to day. People offered anything that wouldn't burn or otherwise contribute to survival. One man displayed only a big jar full of Austrian pfennigs, and an ancient accordion, the bellows rotted through with holes. Every day he was there singing little ditties and fingering the silent keyboard. Children would shout at him, "It doesn't work!" He'd shout back, his fingers dancing over the keys, "Yes! Yes! Can't you hear it? Listen!" We would listen and almost hear it.

One morning an old woman was selling kittens for a dinar apiece. Uncle gave in to Vedrana's sighing manipulations. We walked to the centre of the bridge and sat on the stone bench with our squirming ball of black fur and needle claws. Uncle seized the moment to recite his Drina Bridge history. It was older, he claimed, than anything in Bosnia, built by a Turk (here he drew our attention to the stone scribble above our heads), crossed by numberless armies and bombarded by numberless ordnance, but never destroyed. We half-listened, our minds distracted variously by the kitten, the passing throng, the warming sun, the green patina blooming on the hills above the town, the swirling spring gush of water beneath the parapet. We were told to stay put while Uncle returned to the market to fetch a newspaper. He had promised Blago, who was obliged to take a daily interest in Fascist propaganda.

At that time, I was one to cast harsh judgment on kittens. This one seemed to me especially annoying, able to draw blood yet utterly inconsequential. As Vedrana and my cousins giggled and toyed with it, I felt grown-up and dismissive. I looked away and cast my wise gaze over the world. A German jeep rolled along the bridge toward us, edging past grandpas and mothers and skinny children, and I was at once drawn to the chiselled face and pristine tunic of the young officer. Sun glinted from his brilliantined hair. He seemed in charge of the whole bridge, the town, and the hills beyond, but easily, his gaze generously assessing it all, sweeping it in. His driver too was erect and immaculate, yet he was almost invisible to me. But the young officer, when he caught my eye, expressed in an instant that he was with me, that he shared my disdain for childish things. His gaze held me as the jeep approached; it met me equally and raised me from insignificance. As they drew beside us, he smiled. "*Guten morgen,*" he said, and his jaw muscles fluttered, and the jeep continued past us.

Uncle thereafter let us amuse ourselves on the bridge while he did his round of gawking in the market. It became for us a welcome treat. The bridge offered every sort of human form passing in a stream by the stone bench of the *kapija*. We had a daily arrangement: if the clocktower on the square struck one before Uncle returned, we were to go home without him for dinner. One day my two cousins stayed home and only I and bossy Vedrana were on the bridge. After a time Vedrana said that Uncle was overdue, that we had to go home and eat. I refused to budge. I hadn't heard the clock. I was engrossed in my private thoughts, imagining the lives of those passing before me on the bridge. Vedrana became incensed. I swore at her, and heard a choice phrase of Blago's tumble from my lips. She gaped at me as if struck, her face turned red, and she grabbed my arm and tried to drag me from the *kapija*. I shouted and struggled, tried to wrench free as her nails dug deeper into my flesh. Then we were both sprawled on the stones and she screamed, and when we'd scrambled to our feet I looked and saw blood blooming on her forehead.

There was a silent moment when I was aware of people moving round us, giving a wide berth to our petty dispute. Vedrana then pressed her palm to the bloody gash, and like a spectator I watched the climax of our little drama unfold. I intuited every instant in advance, and the spilling forth of each moment only wretchedly confirmed my helpless prediction. She saw the blood on her palm. She screamed, screamed as if tortured. She called me every kind of monster, repeating it in a piercing stupefied litany, and she staggered off toward home as fast as her righteous hysteria would allow, shrieking of how she was dying, and of how Uncle would beat me senseless. I watched her recede from me on the bridge, watched the running stumble of her progress down the ramp to the river road. I began to hear her tragic speech to Aunt, and to see Aunt's horrified face, and the bloody compresses, and

I was torn between the special hatred reserved for siblings and pure, clear-eyed fear. Perhaps I'd hurt her badly. I could already feel the burning connection with Uncle's backhand.

There was the jeep. Again it was rolling toward me along the bridge. My lieutenant was driving and alone. He pulled aside on the *kapija* and contemplatively set the handbrake. With deliberate movements he lit a cigarette, then he lightly vaulted out of the jeep and moved to the parapet. He smoked, never glancing at me, taking in the vista of river and town, and despite every clue to the contrary I knew that his interest was in me alone. At last he looked at me, said something in German that had the sound of a joke. He winked and addressed the landscape in Serbo-Croatian. "Your girlfriend is big trouble." He looked at me again. "But, perhaps she is not your girlfriend."

"She's my sister, sir."

"Ach! Another trouble."

"Yes sir."

"I heard her screaming. She was bleeding, yes?"

"Yes, sir."

"Yes. Well. Perhaps she is not badly hurt. Come!" He flung his cigarette into the river. "We will go for a ride." He got into the jeep. "Come now. You must come with me. I will fix things for you." He glanced toward the town. "You are a good boy, yes?"

"Yes, sir."

"Quickly now. There is no choice. Let's go!"

He called it his headquarters. Yet he didn't seem able to find his way there. I began to cry and said I had to go home, that my uncle would beat me, and he shouted at me over the rattling engine that

I could not go home to an uncle who beat me, now, could I. That would be complete nonsense. After much driving over roads and muddy trails, we came to the abandoned garage that was once a horse barn. Near it was a ruined house. He performed his deed the first time in the house. Then he sat watching me, smoking, and I watched him, praying he would not shoot me. He said, "What shall we do with you?" So I was introduced to the garage, once he'd determined that the house could not be made secure.

The rest is written. He passed out drunk one night, I smashed his skull and escaped. Within a day of my liberation, I was again in Višegrad, delivered there by a passing peasant woman and her bony horse. I said nothing of my ordeal to her, and when I pushed open our kitchen door and was smothered with desperate tears and kisses and then hard questions, I simply lied. I cried authentic tears and spilled a pale partial truth: I thought I'd nearly killed Vedrana and would be near-killed myself for it, so I bolted. Aunt of course forgave me, and Uncle had to beat me a little because I'd put such fright and despair into all of them. When asked how I'd lived for two weeks, I said the peasant woman had taken me in.

The authorities had done little to investigate my disappearance; a lost child was no novelty and only ordinary drama. A missing German officer was another matter. Within a week of my return, there were notices posted throughout the town offering a reward for information. My terror of discovery kept me awake nights and compelled me to fake illness to stay indoors. Would someone on the bridge that day report my presence in the jeep? It was said the Germans were visiting households and subjecting Serbs and Muslims alike to brutal questioning, that surrounding villages were being searched with a fine-toothed comb. Blago was obliged to endure leading questions from Schmundt and Azzopardi.

At last, word went round that a body had been found. Blago read aloud at dinner a blustering report in the Fascist broadsheet. A German patrol had encountered four Chetniks camped in an abandoned house. The Krauts killed the four easily, taking no losses. A search uncovered a regulation German pistol and behind the house a German jeep. The area was scoured and my lieutenant's corpse found — tortured they said, half-burnt, the skull crushed. I listened, rapt, for any mention of a small boy, but Blago ended and folded the paper and said simply what was easily surmised: Chetniks and village Serbs would now pay the penalty. So I was what might be called free. I had only to stay silent. But that is not how such freedom skulks into the future. I remained undiscovered, but the guilt has shown no limits to its ingenuity. When my friend Mika was killed in Mali Voćnjak, my roiling gut felt it was somehow my fault; that a debt was being paid. And so it has been for other deaths. I set these thoughts down here and now and the understanding in them suggests release, but, truly, there are certain unearthed memories that deserve nothing but reburial. There must be only a turning away from them, and a looking forward.

Blago and Cvijeta sheltered us for two years. Our fortunes fell and rose and fell again. The summer following my German's death was a time of official disfavour for Blago. All Višegrad residents then were beset by new and tormenting regulations from the Germans and Italians. Rumours came of destruction and savagery else-where, but Višegrad at least remained free from battle and the worst adversity.

One day we were in the town with Uncle, sent on a mission for eggs so that Aunt might bake a cake for Saint's Day. From the square we were directed up a narrow street where it was said a woman who kept hens would sometimes part with her eggs for a price. We found the shuttered house and the strange woman living in the dark with the ammonia reek of her chickens. Uncle exchanged some ration coupons for a few eggs, and as we went back down the street he pointed out a roofless building, Višegrad's little synagogue. The windows gaped like empty eye sockets. We peered at the burnt interior. "The Krauts are dogs," said Uncle. "But the Jews don't belong in Bosnia either. They only drain our wealth." His lesson to us was not the atrocity, but his own calibrated approval of it. I remember this day well because in the same street moments later, I soaked my pants in the presence of German soldiers who had stopped Uncle to check his papers. They moved on, and Vedrana's eagle eye swiftly found me out. "Slobo peed himself! You little baby!" Uncle was amused. When we arrived home, Aunt was disgusted. Only Cvijeta gave me sympathy, but I wanted that as little as mocking.

By the next summer, the Italians were gone and we were fully at the mercy of Ustashas and Germans. When knots of brave, fool-ish souls gave in to drunken celebration upon the news of Italy's surrender, they were dragged off and beaten by equally drunk Ustashas incensed by the crumbling of their empire.

On October 5, 1943, I was struck thumbless by a hurtling scrap of steel. The date is in the history books. In a few hours, massed Chetniks drove every Kraut and Croat from Višegrad, and many Muslims too, and left me diminished. As I type this now in Kostreša Hospital I observe the stump: a puckered white scar over the knob of lower joint. The years have taught me to employ my thumb root with impressive dexterity. And now there's my balancing loss, barely a year old, from the bullet at Zabunac railway station. I can report that thumbs are not a necessity.

Uncle and I were deaf for a day after the bombardment. He was otherwise barely scratched. We would not have been in the path of this Chetnik mortar bomb had we not begun to share an affliction. Neither of us could sleep past the wee hours. Awake on our thin mattresses on the floor of the Divjak's upper room, we would share whispers confirming our shared state, then rise together before our patchy exchange of words could stir the wrath of Aunt and set the day on edge. This joint rising became routine. If the weather was fine, we sometimes walked along the road or the riverbank to the bridge. These became my best times with Uncle. In silence or with a few idle words we'd observe the first infusion of light turn the sky over the sleeping town from black to metallic blue, watching as each star succumbed gradually to the day.

The morning of my injury, we had ambled our way under moonlight along the river's edge to the stone ramp that joined at right angles to the bridge. There in the still air below the cool looming arches we sat on flat rocks with the water swirling round.

The bridge drew our gaze in a vaulting rhythm over the Drina to the town square and the shadow figures of two guards, pacing off sleep and the minutes to their dawn relief. Above our heads, at the west entrance, two more guards traded dull phrases between long silences. They'd noted our familiar approach. Uncle and the guards smoked. Matches flared and butt ends traced arcs onto the sliding plain of black water; tobacco smoke lingered in the air and mixed with the river's wet musk. As the moon gave way to a blazing orange-pink dawn, a man with a horse and wagon appeared at the far bend of the river road: the day's first farmer, wondering what he might fetch for the produce he risked taking from his winter store that morning.

Off among the hills there was a rattle of machine-gun fire, echoing along the gorge; then a second burst. The guards above us swore in German and shared a black joke. One called to Uncle, "Granddad! Your boys upriver are shooting each other!" Uncle called back, "Shooting at the moon! That's all! The lads are tipsy!" The guard snorted, "Too early for that!" And perhaps it was, even for a brandied Chetnik.

Then a timeless moment: a long gap that seemed empty but was pregnant with speculation, and a peripheral awareness of the farmer's wagon wheels bumping over dirt ruts. The guard spoke again to Uncle.

"What are you doing down there granddad?"

"Doing? What should I say?"

"Answer the question!"

"We are watching the day begin, as always."

"Come up here! Bring the boy too!"

There was no choice. We had to double back along the bank below the ramp to reach the approach from the road, and this we did, feeling the guards' eyes drilling into our backs. We climbed the weedy embankment to the ramp entry as the farmer's wagon clattered onto the first cobbles. He gave us a good morning nod and receded up the incline, and we followed. The guards stood in silence, watching our approach. Then one of them shouted, staring at the river, and then all four guards were shouting across the bridge to each other. There was an object in the water: a crude raft of sticks and metal drums and sprawled across it two bodies, grey uniformed. Dead Ustashas, the blood still bright on their tunics. We stared at this vision in the rosy morning light. It slid past, pressing its point, then moved smoothly away on the deep current until it became an unrecognizable blot.

The Germans went to their booth and one cranked the telephone and began shouting into it. The farmer now was halting his wagon for inspection. We continued up the ramp toward the guard booth and then before our eyes the wagonload of cornstalks and hay erupted with men and blazing weapons. Uncle threw me onto the cobbles and lay over me. Gunfire left us cowering for what seemed an eternity. Then a lull. Men ran past us, yelled for us to take shelter. And then there was the crump of mortars from the hills, and the sound of explosions from the far bank. We looked and saw the roofs around the town square exploding in showers of red shards. Then the bridge itself was hit. The Drina began to blossom with geysers of muddy water. Rock and mud rained upon us. We scrambled down the bank and under the jutting edge of the ramp, wedging ourselves behind the supports.

A mad scene unfolded, an endless barrage of shells falling upon the river and the Old Town. Chunks of stone were flung from the bridge. Shrapnel impacted like clanging hammers on the rocks before us. Uncle roared at me to stay behind my stone pillar. Then

I was staring at my mangled hand squirting blood like a fountain, the thumb hanging by strings. The pain came like fire. Uncle snatched me to the ground, crouched over me cursing. He cinched his belt round my arm, and my vision swam, and went black.

Višegrad was liberated from the enemy by Serbs, but these hill warriors had with their ballistic zeal risked killing as many town Serbs as retreating troops. The Chetniks had employed an arsenal of captured and abandoned Italian weaponry. It later emerged that Azzopardi had even bartered away tanks and artillery to the Chetniks in exchange for safe retreat through the mountains. The Germans and Croats in Višegrad had come to resemble their captive population: hungry, demoralized and sick of a stagnating war in which the slow progress of misery was the only change. It was as if the Fatherland had forgotten them. And, truly, Yugoslavia was by then the least of Hitler's worries; he was losing in more important places.

As triumphant Serb fighters became swaggering town warlords, the worst misery was reserved for the town's refugee Muslims. Every Chetnik inflamed with two years' grief and rage at enemy atrocities smelled only the reek of collaboration on every living Muslim. Muslims attempting to escape across the Drina that October were lucky to die with only slit throats. Many died the morning of the attack as they tried to flee across the bridge with the retreating Fascists. Uncle later told the story: As I swooned in his arms under the ramp, half-waking with each new blast, the mortar and artillerymen narrowed their sights completely to the bridge. Blood and bodies rained from it, Uncle said. The Drina was tinted red. On the *kapija* the broad tablet incised with

Istanbul's voice was blown into the river. Uncle said that when the big stone toppled, he heard through the din of detonation an undulating roar of triumph from the hills, and a thousand pistols fired at the sky. Through it all, Uncle couldn't help noting that the arches of the bridge stood firm. The shells, he said, seemed to bounce from the massive blocks of stone. In the end, not one span was lost to the Drina.

Not so for my dangling thumb. In the wake of the morning's chaos, it separated for good from my body; as Uncle carried me home, it came loose into his cradling handkerchief, and he threw the whole clotted mess into the river. There would be no miracle of reattachment. In the house, I was spoon-fed sugared brandy to enhance my stupor. Then Blago splashed more brandy onto the wound and stretched the flapping skin over my raw bones and sewed it tight with button thread. He later said he'd learned this art on the battlefield. "Bitolj," he said, and his inflection conjured a universe of suffering and honour. (We all know of Bitolj or are compelled to learn. At this Macedonian town, Serbs died by the thousands, killing thousands more Turks, and the Ottoman armies were at last evicted from our soil.)

Two days after the Chetnik victory, Blago went to the shell-blasted hotel on the main square, the new Royalist headquarters. He wore his old Serb army cap, jacket and medals, and presented the bearded conquerors with a crateful of Banja Luka brandy and a two-kilogram tin of highest grade Arabian coffee. (He'd opened a locked cupboard in the sideboard to retrieve the coffee, his last tin.) I can only assume that he lingered with the heroes and raised toasts to King Petar and offered the same deals that had eased our way with the former invaders. These new troops were, of course, our liberators. Our freedom had an odd cast. For weeks, we children were forbidden to leave the house, and had no desire to. The town seemed to have gone mad. Bodies floated down from the bridge. Gunfire ruled the night and houses burned. Blago would return from the town and talk of corpses on the road. One day, he came home as if in a trance and sank slowly into a chair in the kitchen. Cvijeta greeted him, and Blago stared at her like a cretin, his eyes returning to something in his mind, ranging over it, then he stood and went into the yard and vomited. He sat on the back steps. He refused brandy. He stayed there with his head clutched in his hands, as though he would squeeze something from it, and at intervals he would move to the trash pit and retch again. He avoided the town for weeks and advised the other adults to do the same. This was a man who had survived the First Balkan War. Perhaps the revived memories were the worst of it for him.

Some weeks later, I too witnessed something. Cousins Željko, Goran and I had taken to sneaking into the attic and observing the town and bridge through Blago's binoculars. This particular day cured me of the practice. Željko aimed Blago's glasses at the bridge. He carefully adjusted the focus. Then he stared, and stared, and at last said, "Hadži is on a stick." He gave me the binoculars. It was true. It could be no one else. Hadži from the market, who sold apples and chestnuts. Old crippled Hadži, one leg gone at the knee, only a withered old man with a toothless grin and nicotine tinting his white moustache. And there he was in his underwear, upended on a pole slanting from the Drina Bridge, his leggings brilliant red.

And here I am again, near fifty years on, my feet again on these stones, newly arrived from my non-home and non-village, much closer now to Hadži's age and feeling well beyond it, if not quite so pierced by fate. Here before me on the bridge is the stone tablet, re-erected, the Turkish inscription recarved, history researched and polished up by Father Tito, and now, I plainly see, sullied again by anti-Turks, this time with paint from spray cans. HAJDUK, they spray: OUTLAW. Like tomcats marking a post. FOK ALIJA (a Sarajevo Turk). FOK UNPROFOR (the peace-fakers.) FOK BUSH (though we would like to be American). HVALA ARKAN (thank you to a Belgrade criminal).

Yes. It was here. Here Hadži was on his pole. Just here, opposite the tablet, which *wasn't* here. There. Then. Time is so fluid! Let me try to think. Here I rejected a kitten and accepted the sad coercions of a Kraut. Here I made my sister bleed. If I turn north and look along the bank — is that the house? Is my thumb bone still at the bottom of the river? But which bone would be mine? Some boys are now approaching me from the town side, a little striding knot of them, a clutch of outlaws with peach-fuzz for beards. They radiate disruptive common cause. As they near me, a ripple of bravado moves through them. Their encounter with this strange old man must not be passive. They want respect and approval. Some angle their rosy faces to me grinning, and raise the tripartite salute. "*Živeo Milan!*" And they all join, "*Živeo Milan! Živeo Ratko!*"

I don't know this Milan. We all know Ratko, named a warrior. He was baptized with this name by a priest. Milan can only be Ratko by another name, a smaller Ratko. The boys pass on, breaking my heart because they suddenly return my own boy to me. My Marko.

Again I lived for a time in a house in Višegrad. It had been a Muslim home and lodging house. It was now a refuge to Serb nomads, and run by the Serb who lived next door. He and his wife endeavoured to keep the premises orderly and free from troublesome or overly needy types. The question of their right to the house was, of course, never broached. They did not attempt to collect rent, but those who were willing to do work about the place could get meals in Stamena's kitchen. Their hope, it was clear, was to retain the house at war's end on the merits of occupation and efficient management. Bosnia, Bojan told me over brandy one night, would be seventy-five percent Serb when the war was over. There would be full democracy and increased private ownership. He was as certain of this as he was of snow in winter or the nose on his beefy, bloodshot face.

"We must all take responsibility now, individually, for our future. No one asked for this insanity. We didn't want this killing and turning against our neighbours. But Islam has always held the same problem for us. Always, given a chance, the Muslims will assume power. They know the ways of money and influence. We Serbs bumble along, we're happy enough with our lot, and we drink a little, yes, and sometimes complain that we're hard done by. We were complacent for too long. Meanwhile the Muslims were on the take. They always were, from the time of the pashas. Then Tito got soft on them too, handing them favours. Though many were good people, thank God. Slobo! You know this! We all had good Muslim friends. But the leaders, the ones who poisoned our little friendships, we were powerless against them. I don't believe the stories put out about Bijeljina, Brčko, and Zvornik, it's just more of Alija's propaganda for the West, the same as the Sarajevo bullshit. My cousins in Hrastići saw the Muslims burning Serbs with blowtorches; they burnt their eyes out and cut off their heads. They did! Don't shake your head, Slobo. You see? You don't want to believe. It hurts you too much. Or maybe you've seen them do these things yourself. Yes. Yes. All right then. Slobo. Slobo, my friend. How can we not have vengeance for these things?"

Here we entered a silence and a small shedding of tears, though perhaps not from identical sentiments. We wiped our faces and Bojan refilled our glasses.

"But the killing will be over. The Muslims will be happier elsewhere, in Germany or Netherlands, Turkey even. Some have gone to Turkey from the Sandjak, even before the war, did you know that? They saw the Serb firebrands coming! What can be said? There have been terrible things. Here on the bridge. God forgive Lukić and the others. We were sickened. These peasants watch too much television, that's the truth. No one can stop these dogs once the fighting starts. But it will be over. We are better apart. Better not cheek by jowl. Something happened. The historians will figure it out. But we can't go back to the way it was."

I tried to go back. A winter in Bojan's guesthouse convinced me that Višegrad's labouring Serbness would in the end drive me mad. The town revived all that I couldn't put to rest, heaped upon the new war all the horrors of the old and helped me to imagine that my earliest childhood landscape might restore what I'd lost. On Bojan's radio, Western news competed with Pale and Sarajevo. What came through like a beacon one rainy spring day, on the assured voice of Radio Free Europe, was that Sjecišta was in the hands of U.N. troops: a Safe Zone. It was the market town of my childhood, less than an hour's walk from our village. The idea that I could go home planted itself in my mind, and was watered and nurtured by far-fetched hopes until it sprouted and fanned out like a spray of daffodils.

One morning, I walked out of Višegrad. I crossed the infernal bridge and followed the road westward. After two days of halting progress (inspections, curses and death threats, unaccountable kindnesses), I was at Zabunac, and there was Dušan gazing with contempt at the throng of refugees on the railway platform. Dušan, with whom I'd been at high school in Priboj, Dušan the football heavy who later cracked heads for Tito's youth brigades. We stared, searched our memories. A brief befuddlement unfolded to picking at scabs, old rivalries bloated up with present desperation. His eyes were wild. He became suddenly unhinged, and his deranged display broke the last thread securing another dangling sanity, that of an old Muslim on the platform with his little pistol. So Dušan was shot dead, the guards awoke with the excuse to shoot others, and Slobodan Kušić was utterly de-thumbed.

The Safe Zone of Sjecišta was a pit ringed with fire. The Safe Zone of Sjecišta was shelled and mortar-bombed daily by Serbs in the surrounding hills. Secure within sandbagged bunkers, the U.N. troops watched rooftops implode and walls collapse onto people cowering in basements. Later, they helped pull out the bodies, and still my corpse was not among them and I was obliged to carry on. And later, not too much later, I was found in a truck.

This morning, I read aloud to my nurses from an old letter. Among the letters in my little tin box salvaged from Mali Voćnjak are a handful delivered in 1945 to our house in Priboj by a Partisan officer, a comrade of my father's who had survived the Chetnik assault that killed Father in Montenegro. Father had been a good soldier, rising quickly through the ranks. The bundle of letters contained ribbons and a medal for bravery. The texts themselves are filled mostly with dry or sometimes bloody military reportage from other officers, mixed with dutiful reinforcement of Marxist dogma. The best letters, perhaps even worth something in the war market, though I could never give them up, are from Milovan Djilas, of Tito's command circle. Djilas seemed to have taken a liking to Father; aside from commending his bravery and spouting the usual morale-boosting phrases, he had also confided in him. So this morning I read my favourite letter to my irritable nursing angels, Maja and Hanifa. The guns were quiet, the sun was shining, neither Boško nor Ivan nor Ernad was snoring or complaining, and no screams or cries were heard echoing up from the emergency room. The moment had to be seized.

Dear Comrade Davor:

I hope this will reach you while you're still at Jajce. I write from Vlasenica, and am glad to report that I needn't disguise the fact; our command post here is secure, and we would linger for a good rest if we were not in such a hurry to go on to Kladanj and join up with Tito and Ranković. They told us here that Tito was wounded on Mt. Ozren, in the arm, but not badly; he is carrying on as usual with it slung and bandaged. I am anxious to see him and make my report, though it will be difficult. We've come from the cauldron of the Sutjeska and Tara. The Germans there are scattered and exhausted, but we also took losses. Coming up through the wilderness of Perućica we were eating forest plants and even snails. We could not risk shooting at anything. The worst may yet be ahead of us, but we have something indomitable, something that these miserable Germans can't sustain so far from home: a spirit, an ideal, and the perseverance of village men and women fighting for a collective future. For unity and peace.

My intellect believes these words without reservation. But I can say that on the Sutjeska, plagued by anxiety and days of bloodshed, hearing the Germans killing our wounded whom we had no means of treating or evacuating, I felt despair reaching for me. In Perućica forest, finally stopping late in the night, we posted guards and sank down heavily onto the dry leaves and lay there inert as logs. Here something occurred that has remained lodged in my mind the three weeks since.

After I fell fast asleep, something seemed to awaken me. Suddenly, in my mind Christ appeared; the one from the frescoes and icons, with a silky beard and a look of pity. I knew that this image was synthesized from the stories and impressions of my childhood, but his presence was pleasing to me, as if I found myself in some safe and glowing warmth. I tried consciously to dispel that image, but in vain: it only melted into a still sadder gentleness, firm in its contours. I opened my eyes. Around me, the trees and my slumbering comrades. And silence, endless and lasting, as if there had never been any firing or screaming. I closed my eyes, and there was Christ again — tangible, close enough to touch. I began to speak to him: "If you came into the world and suffered for goodness and truth, you must see that our cause is just and noble. We are, in fact, carrying on what you began. You live and endure in us." As I was saying this, I knew that I was not ceasing to be a good Communist. I'm quite sure that I was awake, and that the image appeared only when I closed my eyes. It never even crossed my mind that this was a miracle, or that miracles occur, though the apparition inspired calm and courage.

Then various thoughts came to my mind concerning the Germans. Some terrible and implacable force was driving them to insane death and shame. Driving us, too, to resist them and pay them back. Yet this passion, this endurance, which lost sight of suffering and death, this struggle for one's manhood and nationality in the face of one's own death, with one's death as a clarion call and an inspiration — this had nothing to do with ideology or with Marx and Lenin.

When the sun rose I suppressed these abysmal thoughts. The morning spread its bright warmth through the forest. The Germans were on the cliff above us. Two Partisans tried to slip through the crags, but the Germans opened fire and we heard screams as their bodies plunged into the ravine. So we prepared to carry on and defend our lives.

Comrade, I know that you have come through similar ordeals — even more, possibly, than I have. Courage and loyalty are what we value most highly, and demand from every one of us. My apparition in the forest may have been brought on by weeks of tension and death, exhaustion, hunger, but I feel that it has awakened something, something that in fact has nothing to do with loyalty or earthly courage: the reality of my suppressed and hidden spiritual self. You once said that the one time in your adult life you called upon God, you cursed him for the loss of your wife to the Chetniks. I understood you. But I see a glimmer of something else, which doesn't inspire cursing or killing. Perhaps when we drive these devils from our soil (they are only human, after all) we can attain our dream of true communality, of peace with our Yugoslav brothers — a true peace of equals.

I've heard it whispered that Christ was the first Communist. How Tito would rage if he heard me say that! For it's true that in spite of whatever else, we must finish the job of war, and be as ruthless as is required. So, finally, I suppose I can only say this to you: courage, my friend! May we survive or die with honour. But I know I will always remember that sad and knowing face, and the peace that surrounded me. I still wonder at it.

Yours in brotherhood,
Djidjo

There was silence as I folded the letter. Then, drifting up the hill, the familiar crack of sniper fire from the Jewish cemetery. From his corner, Boško blew out his lips like an impatient horse.

"There is no God. It is so painfully clear. There is only waiting for God. Who never shows up! God is space creatures, UFOs. They're watching us. They are highly amused. And they are waiting, too, for the real God. Ha! Ahh! Ahhhhh! Nurse! Bring me a god! Any god! My pain is great! A priest! An imam! A mama's tit! Anything!"

At this, Ernad told Boško to shut up, that he was a fool, and had missed the whole point of the letter.

"Djilas is not claiming any God. He admits it was an illusion. What he saw was that peace comes from a state of mind. It's more an Eastern idea. And I don't mean Islam, and I haven't been in a mosque, by the way, since I was fifteen. I mean a Buddhist state of mind. The peace is inner. And it creates outer peace."

"Fat chance," said Boško. "Go and tell that to the boys across the river."

"Your fucking cousins!"

"Yes, Ernad, go. Go and tell my cousins to cross their legs and meditate like a Buddha. It will only improve their aim. Ha!"

"At least you admit it, Boško. Which is the one reason I can sleep in the same room with you."

"Don't paint yourself innocent, dear pussy Ernad. You are such a hypocrite pussy!"

"Thank you, Boško. And you are an asshole with dangling piles, and about as sweet-smelling."

"Fuck your grandmother!"

"And yours, with a Karadjordje Schnitzel!"

"That's enough, you idiots!" said Hanifa. "I want to say something. You must not laugh. I too have seen God. I still doubt Him, it, what I saw. But I saw something. And it was like what Djilas said. It filled me with peace. I was eighteen. I was sitting in my father's car at the roadside on the highway to Modriča. He had gone to relieve himself. We were driving to my Aunt Latifa's house. She died while we were driving there and we didn't know. She died in her kitchen after dinner. Her heart. In the car I saw in my mind a blue light, with light like diamonds shining through it, like hidden stars. Dazzling. But it also gave warmth, it warmed me inside even while it bewildered me. It told me — not with words — but it told me that Latifa was all right. When we got there they told us she had died only an hour before."

"Lucky woman! She's saved!"

"Oh shut your fat mouth, Boško! You're bound for hell, that's certain."

"I have already arrived. We all have."

"Here we go again!" Ernad threw up his hands.

"But it's true."

"A cheap piece of graffiti. 'Welcome to hell.' How original!"

"But Ernad, you great bawling baby, you can't expect war to be original. It's as old as fucking. Only not as dull. Killing is better than fucking. Ask any seasoned warrior."

Maja at last spoke up. "Boško, you are worse than the devil himself. We don't care to hear your hopeless ranting anymore. I don't give one little fart for your ideas. Keep them to yourself! Why should we care for you if all you do is pull us down, tell us there's nothing but to roll over and die? We have all lost so much, more than anyone should bear. I'm sick to death of you compounding our misery with your black ideas. You are only spreading your own wretched outlook like a plague to all of us. I will not stand it any more! Why should we bother? You don't deserve our care! You can fucking well get your own medicines and change your own shitty linen from now on!"

With tears of fury welling, Maja ran from the room. Hanifa glared at Boško and followed her out. We were silent. Boško looked immensely sad, but with a glimmer of superior regret at his abandonment. He slowly shook his head.

"Did she dig a trench for four days in a continuous blizzard? Without one meal? I ask you. I lived on snow and the scraps left over from —"

"Boško, shut up. You've lost this round, yes?"

"I am too tired to carry on, Ernad, in any case. And too deeply hurt."

"Bravo!"

A pregnant silence, then Boško resumed his labours. "Excuse me, Slobo."

"Yes, Boško."

"You know that Djilas helped Tito to murder some thousands of his Yugoslav brothers after the war."

"Don't we all know this, Boško?"

"I just thought I would ask."

"Your point is taken, and not a new one."

"Do you actually think Djilas saw God?"

"How would I know?"

"If there were a God, Slobo, he would not appear to the likes of Milovan Djilas, who happily slaughtered —"

"Shut up, Boško. Just shut up, will you?"

"Why should I?"

"I want to rest. To shut off my mind for a bit."

"Lucky for you if you're able."

"Yes, with luck, and your assistance ..."

"Well then, we'll call it even. For now."

"Why not for good, Boško?"

"For now, Slobo." He smiled thinly at me.

I closed my eyes and gradually drifted into a fitful sleep. I was with Djilas, slogging through a dank forest with Partisan comrades and ragtag volunteers. Monstrous helmeted faces watched us from the trees. As in the nights after my flight from Mali Voćnjak, there were visions of swirling fire and long knives that appeared from nowhere and thrust themselves into me. I woke myself by crying out and heard Boško whining as I drifted off again, this time into a deep black sleep.

Then a light appeared, soft and glowing, and I thought perhaps Djilas's iconic Jesus was coming to mock me, to tempt me with rosy hope. But as the image coalesced it became the face of Tito, bodiless, drifting toward me: his tight-lipped mouth, the stern-daddy creases round the eyes. But this was not the wartime Tito. The apparition hovered close and its outlines became firm, and soon utterly familiar. Here was the Tito whose ageless visage had watched over me for more than thirty years. Here within the same narrow black frame, and secure beneath the fly-specked pane of glass tarred yellow with decades of tobacco smoke. My own Tito, his discerning gaze surveying every small transaction and banal pleasantry passing through the barred wicket of the Mali Voćnjak Post Office. The same Tito who, above reach and reproach, had once ceaselessly surveyed every classroom and railway station and sports arena, hovered over each baggage counter and licence bureau. And then in the dream I became like Djilas, the questing Djilas, searching for meaning and hope. I asked the great Marshal how we might raise ourselves from the abyss and somehow restore peace and prosperity to our land. Tito's eyes shifted and met mine. His brow creased and his lips parted. "More prisons," he said, and vanished.

Chapter Thirty-six

MAY 12, 1995

Dear Toni,

My Bible gathers dust while I reach for Slobo. Like Djilas, like me, he hungers for a God. But the one he's left with is Tito. And his father, the Partisan hero, fighting and dying for Yugoslav unity. More and more blood and drama, our relentless bouncing between sting and balm. I can feel a peace like Djilas' in the company of icons. And of course in the other company: the unspoken warmth that Stefan and I generate around each other, that, in fact, despite the war and all the human irritations, is generated constantly among the brothers.

Regarding peach-fuzz Chetniks: I see them here tagging along after the paramilitaries. And Tito still hangs in our Priječko post office, looking just as spotty.

Plans are afoot. It appears I'll be going on a quick trip into Serb-held Bosnia with Stefan. No, not Goražde, and I'm not insane, but Axel will certainly think so and I'll ask you not to say a word to him. Stefan knows the territory well. The entire region has been securely in Serb hands since 1992. The nearest hot spot is the front lines around the Žepa Safe Zone, which we have no need to approach. So you see, I'm in good hands and the risk is minimal.

We're taking Stefan's niece out of danger — Mirsada, nine years old. She's been living with a family near Borika, a hamlet called Gazići. The villages in the area have always been Serb. The point is to get her out before Ratko makes a move on the Safe Zones and the region becomes chaotic, which they say could happen as early as July.

I want to emphasize that we will be well away from any fighting. If you're talking to Axel and you feel you must say something, then please give him the full picture. We're aiming to leave May 17. We'll stop for a night at Domoševa Monastery near Višegrad, get away early and likely have Mirsada out the same day. We're taking her to Belgrade, where Stefan has found cousins who will take her in. We'll stay a night or two with a friend of Stefan's. I'll phone Vedrana and deliver Slobo's epistle, and I'll try to find out what she knows about Saša and his mother. A full agenda.

xo

Chris

I'd been working in the garden with Stefan, cutting back, clearing winter kill. A cloudburst forced us into the tool shed. As the sheets of rain gusted in he turned to me.

"I must go to get my niece, before Mladić tries to take Žepa."

He asked if he could borrow my car. I said "yes" at once. That was that. When we were back chopping at the raspberry canes I got to thinking.

"Stefan, are you going alone?"

"Demitrios has offered to come. There is no worry. The region is safe."

"How safe?"

He kept slashing at the canes.

"Mladić will take Srebrenica first. If he wins, then Žepa, very possible. But we will go before then."

"I would like to go with you."

He stopped his chopping and gave me a long look.

"I think Abbot will approve. We have your car. And Demitrios is not so young, and bad driver. Life-risker. So. Very good. This is better."

He set to with his scythe again. Then I had another thought. Would I need a U.N. pass? Maybe Martin could arrange it, but it would take time. Stefan dismissed this.

"It is not same as to enter Sarajevo. You must not bring a U.N. pass. Where we cross border there is only Serbs. You will wear your cassock, naturally. Bring only your passport and resident card."

I hadn't thought. It would be the same the whole length of the eastern border. Between Serbia and Višegrad, Žepa, Srebrenica, even Zvornik, the Bosnian border hardly existed. We'd be essentially leaving one Serbia and entering another. If I flashed a U.N. pass it would only raise questions about my sympathies and taint Stefan in the process.

· It was an unstoppable impulse. I didn't want Stefan out there with Demitrios, and me left behind, filling up with worry and speculation and the feeling that I was missing a chance. The chance to no longer be a mere spectator, observing the conflict from Strastanica or my table at Čeko's. It was also an opportunity to be with Stefan outside the cloister, to have him to myself, and it seemed he wanted the same. When he accepted my offer his demeanour changed, as if a burden had been lifted.

Chapter Thirty-seven

The border guards guessed my accent was German. Stefan said I was a novice from Canada. We bantered a little with them. One had relatives in Chicago. As we drove off they urged us to drive carefully. They seemed the nicest boys in the world, not a single fuck or shit or grandmother's pussy. Shouts of *Žive Srbija!* followed us.

Another hour's driving and we were at Domoševa. Big thrusting knobs of rock all around, a grassy hollow, a little white church with badly neglected frescoes and a two-storey Alpine-like residence. The abbot greeted Stefan like an old friend, sat us down with coffee and brandy and talked about everything but the war: sick sheep, roof repairs, the progress of spring growth. He had a formidable patriarch's nose, bits of straw stuck to his robe, mud on his black clodhoppers.

At supper the war finally came up. Two monks out of the eight at table were novices, both ex-militiamen. One said that no one ought to fight for Arkan anymore, that he was "dishonouring Serbs," and the other nodded slowly. When the brothers had dispersed we sat again in the little reception area with Abbot Miloje and he began a monologue to Stefan.

"When will it end, Brother? This madness. Killing and more killing, and these boys can't seem even to grasp what they're doing. Islam is a problem, yes, a turning from truth. But really, we must acknowledge it as an error, a spiritual error, of our own people. Because it's very clear: no matter who is fighting in this war, if they are not Croats or the few Muslims of Croat ancestry, then whether Orthodox or Muslim they are all blood Serbs. This is simply a historical ancestral fact. Mladić is killing Serbs, just as Muslims are killing Serbs. Do you agree?"

Stefan, his brow furrowed, seemed about to speak but Miloje went on: "There is dispute on this point, yes, but it cannot be mistaken. Why do we forget and deny our own history, our Serbian blood? Our Muslims are no less our brothers because they strayed to Islam. They are lapsed Orthodox. They are still Serbs. This cannot be repeated too often. We are destroying our own kin, destroying our Bosnia, and for what? For nothing. A ruined land. The teenagers are brainwashed. Fuck Alija they say, fuck the Koran, but Alija Izetbegović cannot kill our faith, that was never possible. Stupid and intemperate decisions, corrupt and inept leaders, they cannot destroy faith. That is the biggest falsehood of this war. Islam is not a scourge. It's not possible! Our Muslims are the world's worst! They don't even pray, most of them. They drink brandy and eat pork. They marry Christians! But where they were once tainted only by false belief, now we are all tainted with this blind hatred, the endless propaganda, and the endless bloodbath that is the necessary result. And the worst thing is, I can't say this without being called a traitor. I am expected to rally behind these butchers. It makes me weep, brother. This summer

I fear will be a massacre. Mladić is hoodwinking the United Nations. They are blind to it. Arrogant and blind. They imagine Ratko fears them! He has a whole crop of recruits from around Bratunac and Srebrenica, from the Serb villages razed by Orić. They have been burning for revenge for three years. The criminals from the cities, the hellraisers, they have nothing to lose and there's no one to stop them. They each must pledge to kill ten Muslims. I've heard this from boys who come here to be blessed. They think I will be proud of them."

He went on, embellishing his points, driving them home. His steamrollering speech allowed no openings, hardly a chance for us to express concern or sympathy, let alone attempt a challenge. Finally he asked for the news from Strastanica, listened dutifully, then went to bed with hardly a comment, leaving us the bottle.

Miloje was a guru. At dinner his monks knew when to clam up and turn their faces toward his wisdom. He was the complete opposite of Abbot Nikolaj, who ruminates and weighs things and then utters a few unchallengeable words, or says nothing at all.

Stefan and I shared a room, but not a bed. We lay talking quietly in the dark. His opinion of Miloje was succinct.

"It is stupid, defending Muslims because they are Serbs. God does not value persons as Serb or Muslim — or English or something else. All are the same to Him."

At breakfast Miloje cautioned that armed Muslims were sometimes found outside the Žepa safe area, staging night raids on Serb depots and equipment. He noted that anyone could sneak over the mountains at night. The United Nations held the road crossings but most of the demarcation line passed through wooded hills crisscrossed with peasant trails. We would be wise, he said, to stay on well-travelled roads (that was impossible), and certainly to be out of the region before nightfall — which had been our plan all along.

From Domoševa we followed the main road west toward Višegrad. Not far from the monastery we passed through a destroyed Muslim village, every house blasted and burnt. On the walls were Chetnik slogans in sloppy Cyrillic. The ruins were three years old, the rubble overgrown with weeds and brush. Stefan's eyes remained fixed on the road ahead, as if he were willing us on to Gazići and our mission of freedom.

Another quarter-hour of driving and we were entering Višegrad. I thought of Slobo, and Ivo Andrić. It was still only about nine o'clock; I wanted to see the bridge. It would likely be my only chance. I was about to say something to Stefan when he spoke up.

"You must turn right here, for the bridge."

He meant the modern steel bridge, rusty and shrapnel-pocked. As we crossed it I looked south along the Drina and saw stone arches peeking out from around a bend. The road continued past some dilapidated factories until we emerged suddenly close to the riverbank. And there it was, vaulting across blue-green water to the Old Town, with the hills rising behind. I wanted to stop, just for a few minutes. Stefan indulged me. We were confident we'd reach Gazići by noon. We parked and walked to the centre of the bridge. Stefan had never actually set foot on it, though he said he'd read the novel in school.

For a few minutes we stood on the *kapija* while I conjured Slobodan's bombardments, the German lieutenant, the childhood dispute with Vedrana, the impalings. The stone tablet was defaced exactly as the manuscript described, with spray-painted obscenities about Bush, Izetbegović, the United Nations — and now a new one, about "Klinton." When I looked at Stefan he was a picture of suppressed impatience. He had no interest in letting the place enter or move him. Today we were on a journey of correction, of fixing things. A few passersby offered their *God helps* and he dutifully returned them.

There were hardly any people out, and almost no military presence — just some wandering knots of gunmen looking dangerously bored, in sloppy uniforms. The town seemed half-empty, half-dead. As we moved down the long ramp to the road, a VW full of teenagers roared toward us, then slowed to a crawl as it squeezed past, the kids nodding respect with barely suppressed smirks; then they were roaring away again up and across the bridge while pedestrians flattened themselves against the balustrade.

As we were twisting up through the wooded hills west of the Drina, Stefan stopped the car and asked if I had something white. He said we ought to let any Muslims with guns know from a good distance that we were harmless non-combatants. We tied a white T-shirt to a stick and stuck it at an angle in the front grill. Stefan stared at it, then pulled it out. It would only draw attention, he said. Every Serb patrol would wonder who was so anxious to appear innocent. Without the flag we were just another VW with Serbian plates.

We turned off the paved road and headed north for the village of Borika. We would have to ask directions there to Gazići because it wasn't on our map. The route to Borika was a narrow stony track through fir and spruce forest. Twice we came to forks that didn't appear on the map, and sat pondering until we could make a reasoned decision. We were twisting, climbing or descending almost the whole time, easing our way over potholes and rocks, around washouts, and wondering at every blind summit if a speeding Zastava would appear and kill us outright. But the road seemed deserted. We came over a hump and there was a Zastava, partway down a grade, immobile, not quite blocking the road, and four men standing around it.

The group turned as one toward our approach. One had blood on his face and all down his front. The other three were in combat gear. Stefan slowed to a crawl and edged left to squeeze past the car. I couldn't help staring at the injured man. His face was swollen up like a balloon, his eyes puffy purple slits. Fresh blood soaked his beard stubble. His wrists were tied with wire. As we eased by the car the other three nodded, staring flatly at us. Two of them held guns. They were young, maybe still in their teens. In the back seat of the car was another man, who turned to look at me as we inched past. His face was three feet from mine. His nose was mashed and his lower lip was torn, showing broken teeth and a mouth full of blood.

Stefan drove slowly on down the hill. I think he was hardly driving. It was as if he just let us bump over the rocks until the road levelled out and we bumped to a stop. He looked at me, a searching stare, but the searching was directed the other way, into himself. Then his eyes changed. He reversed the car.

"Stefan, there's nothing we can do."

He was already backing toward the Zastava.

"We must try."

"But they could do anything, they could shoot us and no one would know."

"Shoot us? Serbs do not shoot Serb monks."

He must have seen their insignia. I'd seen only brutality. Of course, they had been waiting for us to disappear. Now we were coming up the hill toward them. Stefan stopped the car at a distance.

"Open your door slowly. We must keep hands visible. They know already we are from Serbia, and wearing cassock. We must not show fear. Only brotherhood and compassion. God is with us."

I wanted to refuse but couldn't. I felt the shame of even considering it, the selfish cowardice. We got out of the car and moved toward them. Stefan called a greeting. They just watched us in silence, even the beaten one, his face turned to us as though he could smell more suffering. Finally one of them spoke as we got close, the shortest one; he looked older than the others, with a thin face and scrubby beard.

"*Oče! šta želite!*"

Stefan corrected him, said he was not a priest, only a deacon, but would be happy to be called brother. The short one laughed, a completely false, hard sound, then he continued in Serbian: "What would you like? Brother."

The others were stone-faced. Stefan asked how the men had been injured.

"An accident. We are taking good care of them."

"They've been beaten."

"It's sad, yes."

"We'd like to help them."

"Help them? Brother, they are the enemy. They are prisoners."

"Haven't they been punished enough? They need a doctor."

The Serbs laughed genuinely at this. The leader assessed Stefan with a crooked smile, shook his head.

"They are rapists and murderers. They did this to each other, in fact."

307

The other two gave snorts, shifted their weight and their big guns, stared off into the trees. A pause, the Zastava puttering and spewing fumes, the leader holding his gaze on Stefan. The swollen-faced one said softly that he was not a rapist and was told to shut his *balija* mouth.

"These are vermin, brother. They sneak around like rats. You should thank us. If you came through last night these cunts would be shooting at you."

"I would like you to release them."

"You are asking me to commit suicide."

"We'll take them to Žepa."

"Yoy! What an idiot you are!"

"Would you wish this brutality done to yourself or your family?"

"It won't be done, not by these ones."

"Look at them. Look at their faces."

"I think they look pretty. They look beautiful, don't they? Muhamed! Smile for the brothers!"

"In the name of God ..."

"No no. Fuck that. Go. Get in your car and go. What are you doing here? Maybe you want to fight? Do you want to join us? Janko! Give the brother your gun. Yes! I'm serious!"

The gun was pressed on Stefan. He stood rigid.

"Take it. Are you a Serb? Take the gun, Brother. Where have you been? On a holy mountain? Take the fucking gun!"

We backed off. We turned and went down the hill toward the car. He kept shouting after us, a barrage of abuse, what fools we were, pussy boys, *balije* lovers. We didn't run. It was as if we'd recalled the rules of the wild: don't prove yourself prey. Then there was a pleading voice, the beaten man stumbling after us saying,

"Take me, take me to Žepa." Gunfire began. I think they were firing over our heads, just to enjoy the show. Because it was continuous, it went on and on. We were running, stumbling and falling. We finally got to the car and got inside, and then the beaten man was there, screaming at us, trying to open the rear door with his tied hands. And then he was hit, he was shot. Blood was on the windows. Stefan was trying to start the car. The Zastava was beside us, ploughing through the brush on the shoulder and then onto the road in front of us. It stopped and a soldier got out and he came and stood beside Stefan's window and fired at the ground, into the dying Muslim. He looked into the car at us. He took a few moments to watch us squirming and whimpering.

Then they were gone. I don't know how long we sat there. I remember my heart throbbing like it was going to jump out of me, like the veins in my neck would burst. Stefan had his head against the steering wheel, gripping it with white hands. He was praying quietly. He began a chant, his voice slowly steadying. He kept it going, kept singing right on through my awareness that faith and brotherhood were what had dragged us into this mess and nearly killed us, until I finally broke, gave in to the comfort and was singing the prayer with him. Then we sat again in silence. I stared ahead at the empty road. At last Stefan opened his door and it skimmed over the dead man's feet. He got out of the car, and I knew I had to get out too.

The Muslim was face up on the road, a hole punched through his forehead and other wounds in his chest, blood soaking his shirt and pooled around him in the dirt. Stefan stood over him. He crossed himself and mumbled a prayer. Then nothing. He just stood there, almost motionless. He seemed to be observing the corpse, contemplating it. Even the face. I don't know how he could look at it. There were some bees hovering, alighting on the body. They would disappear into the chest wounds then emerge again. I stared at this, then pulled my eyes away. I wondered if Stefan was in shock. Maybe I was too. I felt separate, separated. But things had clarity. I looked around: just the road, the bushes in spring green, the tall firs pointing into blue sky, and silence, not a bird or a breath of wind.

Stefan spent a long time with the body, crouched in the dirt on his haunches, engaged in some kind of reconciliation or I don't know what. Maybe he was praying that a Muslim soul be allowed into heaven. Maybe for his own forgiveness. He had put his life and mine in danger. He had brought about a man's death, but possibly had saved him from a worse one. The impulse to ease suffering was unassailable. But we should have minded our own business. Of course, Stefan *was* minding his, impeccably: his spiritual business. But God, ever mysterious, decided to rap his knuckles, kill the Muslim, send the other one off for more torture, and have me standing by to take trauma notes. I know that to think this is to reduce the idea of God, that God is an idea of expanding, of countering small and wretched human things. Maybe Stefan felt his faith reduced. He must have. That's why he sat there so long with his legs cramping up, the rocks digging into him. He was trying to extract a meaning from the death and terror, from the corpse itself.

He began unwinding the wire from around the Muslim's wrists. It took him a while, working methodically; it was wrapped many times round, twisted on itself with every turn. When the hands flopped free Stefan stood stiffly and came over to me. We discussed what to do. We couldn't leave him on the road. But it would be pointless to take him to Borika or any other village in

Serb territory — there were no Muslims to identify or bury him. Trying to deliver him to Žepa would mean negotiating Serb, U.N. and Muslim checkpoints. We had nothing to dig with in the rocky soil. We decided we would drag him into the forest, and leave a marker by the road.

We felt obliged to search for identification. Stefan started going through pockets. He was efficient, his face a grim mask, blood flecking his hands. He found nothing in shirt or trouser front. We had to shift the body to reach the back pockets. When we did, a broken section of skull fell open on a skin hinge, and there was the man's brain, open to the sky. I moved away with my gut lurching. When I looked back, Stefan was wrapping the head in my white T-shirt, knotting it up tight. He'd found nothing in the back pockets. We dragged the body into the woods. I wet a towel with bottled water and wiped the blood from the car, then we washed our bloody hands with some brandy given us by Abbot Miloje. Stefan took a good swig of the brandy, but my stomach said no.

We drove on in silence, Stefan again at the wheel. The road climbed and fell, turned back on itself. We twisted along. Finally Stefan spoke, in Serbian, almost to himself: "We were spared. We tried to spare them, but we were spared instead."

I didn't know what to say to that. I just churned with all kinds of thoughts. At last I spoke up, as if talking to the landscape. "Why were we spared? Who spared us? Serbs spared Serbs. Muslims suffered because they were Muslims. Does God spare Serbs first and Muslims second?"

I hated my words as I spoke them. I felt poisonous, like Slobo's relentless Boško in the Sarajevo hospital, dragging everyone through his own misery. Stefan glanced at me and his eyes veered quickly away to the road again. I was staring at his face, his beautiful brow, the clear eyes, the faint acne scars on his cheek, knowing that I loved him then as much as ever and that I had to bare myself. He had to know the blackness that was in me. I had to make him look into it.

"If God is sparing Serbs, then he is killing Muslims. If being spared is not an accident, then neither is anything else. God killed the Muslim. God graced us with this war, and with cancer and AIDS and every other disease, and with famines, the bloated children with toothpick arms. God impales people on stakes and locks them inside churches and burns them. He kills them slowly."

Stefan stopped the car and let me finish. I must have looked awful, red-faced, twisted up with my sacred rage. He didn't even challenge me. There was no fight in him. He stared out at the trees and he said it was all perfectly true. It was indisputable. God made the world, put us into it, put evil within our grasp. God lets us sin, lets us kill each other. We only have to figure out why. "Why?" he said. He gave me a searching look. "I don't know. *Ne znam.*"

He got out of the car and looked off into the landscape. We were on the edge of a ridge, the land falling away from the road, then rolling up again in scraps of forest and meadow. A few patches were fuzzed green with spring planting. Stefan abruptly left the road. Grabbing at bushes, he scaled a little hill up to its grassy summit. He stood facing the valley, turned to glance back at the car, then disappeared down the far slope.

I shut off the engine and went after him. He was sitting on the grass. I lay down near him and closed my eyes. I tried to empty my mind. It was easier with my eyes open, if I just watched the sky. I began to feel my weight again, felt my body against the ground, the sun's heat on my robe. I thought of the ground under me, earth, the Earth. I saw the dead man's face at the car window, pleading. I stared into the clear sky. The endless depth of blue. Then no depth at all, just empty perfect colour like a sort of blindness. Then a white cloud to break the spell, and musty heat rising through the tall grass. I turned my head and Stefan was looking at me. We watched each other's faces, like we were searching for clues.

The grass stirred. Stefan stood and offered me his hand. He pulled me up, then he was clambering down the hill toward the car. I said I would drive. Under way, we were quiet. Stefan pored over the map. We came to a crossroads, Stefan pointed right and shortly we were entering Borika. We stopped at a *bife* and were told Gazići was fifteen minutes away. We washed up and had some coffee, pouring a little Domoševa brandy into it. It was about one in the afternoon. We'd left Domoševa just four hours before.

Gazići was a hamlet of perhaps twenty houses scattered along a stream. The family lived in a four-room house, a small cornfield and orchard climbing the slope behind. Mirsada shared a room with the couple's two little girls. The mother had been a neighbour in Stefan's hometown of Sokolac. She said she and her daughters would likely go there soon to stay with relatives. The father served with the local militia and wasn't at home. Maybe he was out rounding up Muslims. We ate a meal of sausage and cheese pie, thick yoghurt. She didn't skimp. This was the send-off lunch. She made the girls stand by their chairs until Stefan had said a prayer. We both ate as though we'd been starved. The rich food, the occasion, the girls' chatter, made the events of the morning feel impossible, like a dream.

In the car Mirsada was mostly silent, asking wary questions now and then about Belgrade, who she'd be staying with, whether

Stefan would visit. He tried to be jaunty and reassuring. We crossed into Serbia without incident, two monks and a Serbian-ized little girl. We called her Krstina, her mother's name. In Požega we found a motel, a room with two beds and a folding cot, but Mirsada wanted to sleep with her uncle. I slept as though in a coma for a few hours, then I was jolted awake. Stefan was snoring quietly. I looked and saw Mirsada curled up against his back.

Chapter Thirty-eight

Our soiled cassocks went into our bags. We entered Belgrade dressed like regular citizens. Mirsada was delivered to an apartment in Novi Beograd, a huge building out near the airport, where she was lavishly welcomed by a woman with crimson lips and painted brows, a heap of brassy hair. Her own child, a teenage daughter, was at school. Mirsada was shown her room, her very own, with a pink bedspread and matching frilly curtains. We stayed for some coffee. Stefan kissed his niece at the door. She did a good job of being a brave girl, but she looked lost. She had not seen this woman since infancy.

The gap between haves and have-nots in Belgrade was everywhere apparent. Cars were either Yugos belching smoke or shiny Mercedes and Audis. There were long queues outside stores. People were in the street selling clothing, pots and pans, old magazines, pictures off their walls, anything expendable, in the hope of a few dinars.

Stefan's old school friend was Pero, a dapper bachelor who spent hours on the phone in his office. We stayed two nights in his apartment overlooking the Kalemegdan Fortress. He had some awful erotic paintings, but a good music collection, including Hilandar chant. He cooked lavishly for us. We felt like we'd joined the haves. Stefan made Pero pause before each meal as we recited our Strastanica grace. They'd known each other at Belgrade University, before Stefan entered the seminary. It was instructive seeing him with Pero, watching him laugh, allowing old innuendoes. Later I asked Stefan probing questions until I broke through to some candour.

"Pero was born to make money. He's a manipulator. Impossible to live with."

"You lived with him?"

Stefan considered the velvety wallpaper.

"We were students. It was very brief."

We had to share a double bed — either that or make a deal out of one of us using the couch. I knew Stefan wanted me not to touch him. My mind — my cerebral mind — agreed with that. The other part bounced to attention when I got under the sheets next to him. He was amused, and utterly intransigent.

"You know we can't. And why? Why do we need it?"

By then I did need something. I went to the bathroom and wanked myself like a teenager. Back in bed I kissed the back of his neck, a gentle peck. He pretended to be asleep. Then he *was* asleep, with his soft snore, while I lay listening to traffic sounds and began to twitch, running from the bullets all over again.

I telephoned Vedrana from Pero's. Slobo had been occasionally in touch with her through Martin, but she hadn't known anything about the manuscript. I dropped by her apartment the same afternoon to deliver it. Slobo had said she had lymphoma. I wondered what sort of treatment she'd be getting under current conditions, and I was half-expecting a gaunt and ravaged woman, but she was not that — more tough and sinewy, a good head of silver hair, and eyes that watched intently as she listened. I discreetly searched her face for any sisterly resemblance to Pimm, without much luck, beyond the dark brown eyes. She assumed, because of the Martin connection, that I was a reporter. I wished that I could have told her more about the state of Slobo's health, when he might get out of Sarajevo and so on, because these were the questions she asked.

Her building was a dowdily ornate prewar block near the Old Town. She served me tea in her parlour. On the wall behind her were photos of children, babies, a uniformed man and, I thought, the same man older. I didn't ask, but her aura was unmistakably widow-like. The photos on display were not the ones I was hoping to see. I thought she might have the ones taken in 1945 in Priboj, of the infant Saša, and herself, and Slobo, and perhaps some shots of Slobo as an adult. I'd brought along Pimm's birth certificate, and a photo of him at thirty-five.

I told Vedrana Pimm's story: the dates and places, registered as Saša Kožić or Košić, father missing, mother and child leaving Yugoslavia. The mother's death and Saša's adoption. How Pimm died wondering about his ancestry. I said that Slobo's manuscript mentioned her little brother Saša Kušić, and their father, killed in Montenegro, and the mother who visited Priboj and took photos. Vedrana watched me.

"There are so many Sašas. And orphans. So many."

" Do you recall the mother's name? Was it Ljiljana, or Lili?"

She shook her head.

"It might have been. We met her only briefly. He called her his rabbit or something, a pet name. We didn't like her much. She took all of Father's attention."

I took out my photo of Pimm and gave it to her. She perused it awhile and then went to a closet. She returned with an old tin biscuit box, sat down and pried it open. She went through the loose photos, extracting some and handing them to me one by one: Slobo at various ages, teen to adulthood. We agreed he didn't look completely unlike Pimm. Vedrana used a magnifying glass, moving it from Pimm to the Slobo shots.

"The nose, a little. And these heavy brows, the dark eyes. The chin, no, not at all. And Slobo's face is longer. But brothers often look so different."

From an envelope she took four small snapshots.

"This is Priboj."

One photo showed an infant in Vedrana's arms. The shot was blurred, the faces indistinct. Another was of Saša held by his Aunt Marija, with Slobo and a scowly looking Vedrana posed beside them. The two others were of Saša on a blanket in the grass. He was naked, saucer-eyed, mesmerized in one shot, delighted in the other. He looked like a thousand other pudgy, happy babies. His eyes were dark, like Pimm's. His little penis pointed its intact foreskin at me. I stared and stared. I resisted the urge to ask for Vedrana's magnifying glass. I was thinking, Is that the same penis? The same eyes? Are those the lips? Thirty years later, September 1975. I sat on a bench behind the Conservatory and Pimm wandered by. Then he wandered back, and I convinced him to come home with me.

"You are quite taken with this photo."

I looked up at her and felt the blood in my cheeks.

"You were close to your brother."

A flicker crossed her face. Maybe she caught the truth.

"Please, you may keep the picture if you wish."

Chapter Thirty-nine

Stefan was called in from the tomato patch today. I glanced out at the garden and saw him running, then he burst into the kitchen and straight through to Abbot's office. His parents were on the phone from Ilijaš. He'd been unable to reach them for over a year. It was a birthday call, two days late, but it still felt like a miracle. His mother had just turned sixty. Stefan was closed in Nikolaj's office for maybe ten minutes before the connection was lost. He emerged and reported to a knot of waiting brothers. Both were in good health. The town was still secure. He'd been able to tell them about Mirsada.

The story of Mirsada remains an edited one. Only Nikolaj knows, and only from Stefan, about what we encountered on the Borika road. We haven't spoiled the tale of liberation. We still don't know how to think about the truth, let alone how to tell it. If it is told, it will be by Stefan. It's a story for Serbs to share if they're able. Now there's the news from Srebrenica, more horrific with each report. We pray that it's not true, and blame the media, the warlords, the United Nations, all the powerful ones. Not the little ones, the village Serbs, the boys in the woods with guns.

I'm beginning to find corpses in my dreams. They're in my bed, or in the garden, or I'm driving in a car over them. Sometimes it's all mixed up with Pimm. Pimm dead or almost dead, and talking to me, his mouth moving silently. Sometimes I wake up suddenly, like I've been hit or stabbed, and the dream is just impressions that refuse to focus. I might be soaked in tears. The tears flow out of my eyes and I just lie there wondering what it's about, as if someone is pumping it through me. If I can't sleep I go into the church and light some candles, then just sit, looking at the icons. I might find Stefan there too, or other brothers. We don't say a word. Sometimes a warmth envelopes me, seems to be enveloping everything. It arrives and overtakes me and I think, even as I'm melting in its presence, What is this? It's obviously not a full experience of the world — not of this one at least, the one we're stuck in.

Yesterday I went up to the lookout with Stefan. The wind was amazing, almost hot, full of forest scent. We sat on the bench by the cliffside and looked over the waving trees toward Priboj and Rudačac. It's different now, looking at this landscape. There's the usual intensity of seeing, but the meaning of what happened sits there now under the trees, under the same sky: that here's no promise of life. Slobo said it. Chance divides the actual from the true. Life is the blink of an eye.

Chapter Forty

In December our leaders and diplomats put a stop to the war. There are said to be 250,000 dead, three million homeless. Four years too late, the blue-helmets have a peace to keep.

I'm six months a novice. Nikolaj instructs me, I consult the recommended texts, and they fuel or challenge my private devotions. I still don't consider myself a sinner, which is my most unspeakable secret here, and probably my greatest failing. Stefan alone knows this about me. I'm in the antechamber of faith, still doubting much of the Christian project. It's wrong to think that all holy men and women are blind believers. The brothers have knowledge of themselves and each other that will never be shared openly. We live, like any other tribe, by conventions that glide on the surface, hiding all the stuff beneath that toils away at the unacceptable. The final vows will be my most perilous leap, but Stefan counters that simply: "It doesn't hurt."

Last September, we had a little lapse in the loft of the barn. We'd been milking goats. The day was warm, the hay was fragrant, we rolled around and sweated under the sun-baked roof with the straws scratching us and sticking in our hair. It was a ten-minute madness. Then we remade ourselves into goat-milkers. Stefan said we should not let it happen again, and it hasn't, so far. It's an impulse, not a true need. It was something like this with Pimm, in another world.

Axel visited a few weeks later. He learned that he didn't like seeing me in this place, seeing my love of it, and it was impossible for him to hide it. He stayed two nights. At meals he and Stefan eyed each other, breaking into tight smiles if they had to exchange words. We never got to Dubrovnik. If we had, the fun would have been terribly forced. I drove him to the bus station in Pljevlja, we hugged goodbye, and as I drove back I knew I might not see him again.

Chapter Forty-one

4 JANUARY

Dear Miss Perović,

I hope you will share this letter with the young man who delivered Slobodan's manuscript to me in Belgrade. I've heard good news. Slobo is released from hospital and living in a temporary arrangement with a friend he knew at Sarajevo University, where you likely know he studied Balkan and Slavic literature before the Post Office came to his rescue. Ivan was with him in the hospital, and now they are in care of Ivan's wife and two daughters. I suppose they are living like princes, or as near as Sarajevo can offer at the moment.

So you see he has survived the bombardments and everything else. In November he was able, at last, to get the drugs needed to treat his headaches and depressions. He has a plan to visit me in March, and then he will go on to his daughter, now in Niš. I have not seen Slobo since 1989, when his wife was taken so suddenly, and now his manuscript and your work on it have brought us together again.

Your Canadian friend said he was living in Sandjak region. He may wish to know that Slobo will probably make a visit to Priboj in April or May. Our cousin, Goran Kušić, lives there still with his wife and grown-up children. The house is still there too, though not in the family. I mean the house where we stayed in summer and fall of 1945 and met our little brother, Saša, who has drawn your friend so deeply into our family history. He must feel free to ring Goran and Justina at (313) 447-937. Slobo would be happy to talk about our brother who might have ended his days in Canada, or at least to share his sketchy memories of Saša from Priboj.

I would like to thank both of you for the help you have given to Slobodan, and I regret that I have not written sooner with this. My health has taken a downturn, but I feel stronger these past few weeks. What a great amount of careful work you have done with this translation, Miss Perović. I made a start on the English, but then your copy of Slobo's typescript came and I progressed more quickly, even with Slobo's deletions and peculiar spellings.

It is very strange for me to read of my brother's suffering in this war. I sorrowed terribly for him, and for our ruined Bosnia and Yugoslavia. Some parts I could hardly make myself read. But sometimes the passages about our childhood took me out of my sadness. Even among Fascists, our time in Višegrad was not always terrible.

I can say with certainty that my brother's memory diverges from my own with regard to 1941-45. In particular, I would like to correct his memory of a dispute between us on the Turkish bridge at Višegrad. The incident as written is completely back-ward, and I have told him so recently over the telephone. It was Slobo who suffered a wound to his forehead when he fell on the stones, and it was Slobo who ran home to the house, while I stayed on the bridge and was propositioned by a German officer who pretended sympathy with our little fight. I refused to get into his car. My memory is that the same Kraut was later responsible for the murder of a girl, in the woods near Dušče. So, there is some fiction in my brother's story — aside from the obvious fictions about eyeballs in baskets, and deaths that did not actually occur, but might have, and ghosts floating out of old wells. Some say the eyeballs were real. I know that the soldier named Spaso is real enough. If boys (not all boys, certainly) can imagine a horrible thing, and there is no one to stop them, they will try to do it.

However, it was I who made my brother bleed on the Drina Bridge, and it was he who called me all sorts of names and ran hysterically home to our aunt and uncle. I was not inclined, at any age, to behave as he describes. I pushed him because he refused to come home for dinner, and he fell. Otherwise he would not have been hurt, and I would not have had a smiling Kraut telling me my business. But foreigners have always told us how to keep our own house, and have usually murdered us while doing it.

Slobo was obsessed by the Višegrad bridge. He never wanted to leave it at dusk or when mealtime came. I remember too, when I stood on the bridge, with the water flowing below and the sky above, suspended there in the middle, I could sometimes feel that the war was not so bad, or so close. It was a child's escape. But we are all captivated and appalled by our beautiful Drina and all it represents. It joins us and divides us, as Slobodan said. At least this war is finished. I hope we're not asked to survive another one.

Sincere regards,

Vedrana Brković

Chapter Forty-two

I have two Sašas framed on my desk. Or one. Child and adult. When I look at them the question of connection seems meaningless. I mean the question of proof. My heart is stirred by both. Pimm's picture is so familiar, and the loss and the regret are now so familiar too: the idea that if more care had been taken, his care and my care, he might possibly have lived. If we'd talked more, about staying safe. That will always be with me. But when I look at the child, he's all future. All the pain and risk and love and joy is potential. I want to pick up this Saša and cradle him in my arms, keep him from harm.

I've been to see Slobo. Goran and Justina Kušić had me to Priboj for a midday meal, served at a table on the grass beside their hillside house, with its view down the greening valley. Their daughter joined us, with a taciturn husband and three young children.

Slobo is a ropy, long-limbed, silver-bearded wolf of a man. Even his toothy smile reminded me of an old dog's. There was pain in the drawn-back lips, and endurance, the memory of beatings and the relief that, for the moment, the company is good and the danger far away. He's impressively nimble with his thumbless hands — the children stared as he wielded knife and fork.

He looked at my photo of the adult Pimm with interest, then it was passed round the table. They searched the face of a stranger. In person, Slobo seemed somewhat less like Pimm than Vedrana's photos suggested, though with the beard it was hard to say.

After the meal we went on a walk apart from the group. Then we sat in the sun on two sawn-off stumps at the edge of the woods. We could hear the little party still going on at a distance, the children at play. Slobo asked about the monastery. He'd been to Strastanica while still a teenager in Priboj, shortly after the war. Sitting alone with him, I began to feel tongue-tied. I felt such a daunting respect, an awe, for what he'd suffered, for what he knew about the world, and for the words he'd found to describe it. There seemed no way to say this to him, to say what it did to me. Instead I rattled on about Pimm: how we learned that he was Saša from Priječko, his hope of coming here, the impossibility of it. So I came instead. And here I was, four years later, sitting on a tree stump with Saša's possible brother.

Slobo considered me.

"And how does it feel? Here with Saša's possible brother."

"I wish he could join us."

"You came here to find him again. Correct?"

"I guess I did."

"And you did not find him."

I stared into the woods. Dark branches and luminous green.

"And you can't go back. No. I will never go back, to my village. Nothing is there."

We sat quietly. Then Slobo strode into the woods and began breaking deadwood off the trees. He called to me.

"Maybe I will join your monks. Do they worship Tito?"

"Abbot was a Partisan."

"I will join!"

We walked back to the house, Slobo's loping gait taking him ahead of me. He dumped his armload of kindling by the firepit and called to his cousin. "Goran! Get some brandy for this Kanadski monk."

We had a round of Goran's homebrew, and the taciturn husband at last spoke to me directly.

"Can you tell me, Brother, why you chose Yugoslavia? How do you hold belief in God in this nest of vipers? I can think of better places."

I was speechless for a moment, everyone eyeing me. The children went quiet. Slobo grinned his wolf grin. I coughed and spoke to my brandy glass.

"I don't believe."

It was the greatest joke of the afternoon. The men roared. The women shook their heads like I was a delinquent child. Goran wagged a finger at me.

"Don't drink too much Brother Chris. Who will save you on the road home?"

He refilled my glass.

Acknowledgements

In 1991 I knew almost nothing about Yugoslavia. That began to change when Brian Pronger, my partner of twenty-nine years (and counting), invited me along to a conference he was attending in Dubrovnik. For many reasons, if this book could reasonably be dedicated to one person, it would be to Brian. But *Drina Bridge* owes a greater debt to the dozens of others whose knowledge and generosity ensured that what I'd started came to a confident finish — confident, but necessarily imperfect. Any historical errors or cultural distortions must finally be my responsibility.

Regarding gay monks: we're all aware by now that in every human community, gay people (visible or not) form at least part of the picture. That said, I should add that the Serbian Orthodox clerics and monks who generously accommodated me in Ontario and in Serbia will know better than anyone that *Drina Bridge* is a work of fiction.

My heartfelt thanks to all who have advised, assisted and supported me, in Canada, the U.S., Bosnia, Serbia and Croatia. Foremost among the many: Goran Ćirić; Bishop Georgije; Father (now Bishop) Milutin; the monks of Kaona Monastery; Demir

Selmanović; Edin Bajrić; Father Dionisije; Paul Russell; Goran Simić; Višnja Brčić; Davor Miličević; Slobodan Kuzević; Enes Jakić; Maja Mihić; Vladimir Vasojević; the monks and nuns of Studenica Monastery; Nermina Harambašić; Daniel Gelfant; Dubravko Naumov; Stanko Bilkan; the border guards at Ljuba; Milan Bilkan; Alex and Hana Ivanišević; Srdjan Bukvić; Braćo; Ostrog Monastery; Sopočani Monastery; Dobrun Monastery; Tavna Monastery; Lovnica Monastery; Rupert Schieder; Natasha Vasiljević; Sonja Carr; Gordan Marinković; Paddy Stamp; Bahrija Alić; Larry Fineberg; Jennifer Glossop; Rick Archbold; Saša Daničić; Sonja Pastuović; Mark Cornwall; Dan Healey; Sister Justina; Sister Ljiljana; Mike Grippo; Milan Pajić; Aleksandar Lukać.

A special thanks to my dedicated and admirably tenacious agent, Anne McDermid; also to Michelle Benjamin, Lynn Henry, Jamie Broadhurst, Angela Leung, Teresa Bubela and the many others at Raincoast who believed in the book and made it real; and to my editor, Martha Sharpe, who changed my mind and sharpened my pen.

Finally, to Babette Babich, whose love of Dubrovnik started the ball rolling.

Books consulted:

Ivo Andrić, *The Bridge on the Drina*, University of Chicago, 1977.

Svetlana Broz, *Good People in an Evil Time*, Other Press, 2004.

Boris L. Davidovich, *Serbian Diaries*, Gay Men's Press, 1996.

Milovan Djilas, *Wartime*, Harcourt Brace Jovanovich, 1977.

Slavenka Drakulić, *The Balkan Express*, HarperCollins, 1994.

Janine di Giovanni, *The Quick and the Dead*, Phoenix, 1994.

Tom Gjelten, *Sarajevo Daily*, HarperCollins, 1995.

Misha Glenny, *The Balkans*, Viking, 2000.

Radmila Gorup & Nadežda Obradovic (eds.), *Prince of Fire: Contemporary Serbian Short Stories*, University of Pittsburgh, 1998.

Roy Gutman, *A Witness to Genocide*, Macmillan, 1993.

Peter Handke, *A Journey to the Rivers*, Viking, 1997.

Michael Ignatieff, *Blood and Belonging*, HarperCollins, 1994.

Tim Judah, *The Serbs*, Yale University, 1997.

Anthony Loyd, *My War Gone By, I Miss It So*, Doubleday, 1999.

Peter Maass, *Love Thy Neighbor*, Knopf, 1996.

Noel Malcolm, *Bosnia: A Short History*, New York University, 1994.

David Rohde, *Endgame*, Farrar, Straus & Giroux, 1997.

Laura Silber & Allan Little, *The Death of Yugoslavia*, BBC, 1996.

Chuck Sudetic, *Blood and Vengeance*, Norton, 1998.

Dubravka Ugresić, *Culture of Lies*, McArthur & Co., 1999.

I am indebted to Ivo Andrić for my title, and to Andrić and Peter Maass for their chilling descriptions of the Višegrad impaler at work.

A portion of the Milovan Djilas letter in chapter 35 is excerpted from *Wartime*, by Milovan Djilas, translated by Michael B. Petrovich, Harcourt Brace Jovanovitch, 1977. Used with permission. The quoted passage begins "After I fell fast asleep ..." and ends with "... their bodies plunged into the ravine."

I gratefully acknowledge financial support from The Canada Council for the Arts, the Ontario Arts Council and the Toronto Arts Council.

Jim Bartley